She *would* sta

Paige didn't know
he was it would m
didn't dislike him any more, she *hated* him!
Totally, utterly, completely, and she would have
her day with this man! She nodded a mental
promise to herself. If it was the last thing she
did, if it took years, she would bring Declan
Stone to his knees.

Dear Reader

In February, we celebrate one of the most romantic times of the year—St Valentine's Day, when messages of true love are exchanged. At Mills & Boon we feel that our novels carry the Valentine spirit on throughout the year and we hope that readers agree. Dipping into the pages of our books will give you a taste of true romance every month...so chase away those winter blues and look forward to spring with Mills & Boon!

Till next month,

The Editor

Helen Brooks lives in Northamptonshire and is married with three children. As she is a committed Christian, busy housewife and mother, her spare time is at a premium but her hobbies include reading, swimming, gardening and walking her two energetic, inquisitive and very endearing young dogs. Her long-cherished aspiration to write became a reality when she put pen to paper on reaching the age of forty, and sent the result off to Mills & Boon.

Recent titles by the same author:

SWEET BETRAYAL
AND THE BRIDE WORE BLACK
A HEARTLESS MARRIAGE

BITTER HONEY

BY
HELEN BROOKS

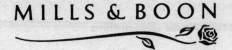

MILLS & BOON LIMITED
ETON HOUSE, 18-24 PARADISE ROAD
RICHMOND, SURREY TW9 1SR

First published in Great Britain 1993
by Mills & Boon Limited

© Helen Brooks 1993

Australian copyright 1993
Philippine copyright 1994
This edition 1994

ISBN 0 263 78394 4

Set in Times Roman 10½ on 12 pt.
01-9402-51520 C

Made and printed in Great Britain

CHAPTER ONE

'PAIGE? Your stepfather's party... There was some-thing I forgot to tell you...' As her mother's soft warm voice faltered to a halt at the other end of the line, Paige felt her antennae begin to buzz. She knew that note of apologetic persuasion from the past. Whatever she was about to hear, her mother knew she wouldn't like it.

'Yes?' She kept her voice bright as she mentally prepared for one of her mother's disasters.

'It's Declan.'

'Declan?' It was going to be worse than she thought if it had anything to do with him! She heard the rasping, shrill edge to her voice as she said his name and forced it a pitch lower as she continued, 'What's he got to do with Gerald's fiftieth birthday party? I thought he'd forgotten where you both lived! You don't mean to say he might actually be going to honour us with his presence, do you? America's loss is our gain and all that?'

'Paige...' The deep sigh that fluttered down the line caused her a moment's guilt. But only a mo-ment's—they *were* talking about Declan Stone! 'Please don't be like that, darling. Declan is Gerald's son, after all. It's only natural he should be at his father's party.'

5

'I couldn't agree more,' Paige said tightly. 'It is also natural that he should visit you both occasionally, maybe call in at Christmas or the New Year, anything!' The shrill note was back and she took a long deep breath before continuing. 'How long has it been since you've seen him?'

'A few months,' her mother prevaricated vaguely. 'But he's a busy man, Paige.'

'Busy man, my foot!' The sense of rage the mere sound of Declan's name induced was causing her cheeks to burn. 'He flies between America and England at least once a month to my knowledge. Do you honestly mean to tell me he can't come and see you more often than he does? The man's a philistine. I know——'

'Darling, please, please. Don't upset yourself. Declan is Declan. Accept him for what he is. I have.' The gentleness that was an innate part of her mother's character reached out to her over the distance that separated them. Paige could just picture the anxious eyes and soft mouth. 'I don't know why you've always disliked him so strongly. He isn't that bad really.'

It took all of Paige's considerable will-power to stifle the hot words that sprang on to her tongue, but stifle them she did. She knew from experience that anything she might say would only cause her mother distress, and that was the last thing she wanted to do. 'I'm sorry, Mum, I can't really talk now,' she said quickly. 'I'll call you back later.'

'No need.' Her mother sounded grateful that the matter had been dispensed with so easily. 'I just wanted to let you know, that's all. Will you be arriving at six still? Your room's ready, and are you sure Matthew doesn't want to stay over?'

'I'm sure.' Paige was immensely glad technology hadn't yet provided the means for her mother to see her face as they talked. For all Brenda Stone's somewhat woolly approach to life, she could be like the original British bulldog where her only daughter was concerned. She thought Paige had just taken a childish dislike to Declan that had grown with the years. That was fine and exactly the way Paige wanted it. She would walk through fire before she revealed the real reason she loathed Gerald's son with an intensity that bordered on hate.

'Goodbye, then, dear. We'll see you tomorrow,' her mother said quickly. 'And, Paige?'

'Yes?' There wasn't more, was there?

'Don't be too hard on Declan, darling. You haven't seen the man in ages, and Gerald is thrilled he's coming. Don't make waves; try and be civil.'

'I'll try.' Her voice lacked conviction and she caught the soft sigh as her mother replaced the receiver with another stab of guilt as her eyes darkened with anger.

Blow you, Declan! she thought savagely as she glared aggressively at the inoffensive phone. Why did you have to turn up like the proverbial bad penny?

She could never hear his name without her mind winging back over the years to that first time she had seen Gerald's son. She had been just sixteen, painfully shy, her face covered in freckles and the odd adolescent spot, huge horn-rimmed glasses hiding her eyes, her hair pulled back in a tight unbecoming ponytail and a heavy metal brace on her front teeth.

He had been a devastatingly adult twenty-four, cool, charming and, although not exactly handsome, with something dark and mysterious in his make-up that appealed to a romantic sixteen-year-old far more than film-star good looks.

It had been her first visit to Gerald's beautiful country house in rural Hertfordshire since he had started courting her mother two months before, and she had been utterly overwhelmed by the opulent lifestyle this quiet, unassuming friend of her mother's was apparently used to living. So had her mother. The two of them had crept through the vast, exquisitely furnished rooms with something akin to awe straightening their faces until her mother had shrugged resignedly. 'We are what we are, Paige,' she had said matter-of-factly. 'Let's just enjoy the weekend away from the city grime.' And so they had, until she had overheard a conversation between Declan and his father two hours before they were due to leave.

Gerald had thrown a pool party in the massive grounds of his estate, a riotous barbecue by the enormous swimming-pool in order for some of his friends to meet her mother, but Paige had developed a headache and returned to the house, half hoping, she admitted secretly to herself as she entered the huge French doors at the back of the house, that she might see Declan alone before he returned to his flat in London. Not that she harboured any notion that he might be interested in a plain Jane like her, but she just wanted to look at him again before they had to leave. It was her first experience of a 'crush' and she was finding it painful.

'I don't understand you, Father!' She heard Declan's voice first, hard and low and throbbing with intense anger. 'What the hell are you thinking of?'

They must be in Gerald's study, she thought quickly as she stood hesitating in the enormous wood-panelled hall, and obviously having some sort of disagreement. She'd better go back to the party.

She was turning to leave when Gerald's voice stopped her in her tracks. 'I love Brenda, Declan.' The older man's tone had been one of patient persuasion. 'What's wrong with that?'

'Nothing.' She heard a sound like a chair being scraped back abruptly on the parquet flooring. 'You're still a young man, Father; I would expect you to take your pleasure where you find it. But marriage? That's a whole new ball game. You've only known the lady eight weeks! What makes her so different from all the other gold-diggers who have been after you since Mother died?'

'That's enough, Declan.' Now Gerald's voice was tight with irritation. 'Brenda's a wonderful woman and I love her. The others *were* different. I enjoyed their company and we had some laughs but there wasn't one I could envisage spending the rest of my life with. Until now.'

'Well, isn't that just dandy?' The voice sounded closer, as though Declan had moved towards the half-open door, but for the life of her Paige couldn't move. She stood, trembling slightly and white-faced like a small frozen statue. 'You don't think it's wishful thinking, do you? I hate to say this, Father, but I don't trust that dewy-eyed helpless angle the lady does so well. I've got a nasty idea it's hiding the pound signs in her eyes. I don't like her and I don't trust her, and as for that awful daughter!' There was a harsh bark of a laugh. 'Do you seriously expect me to acknowledge *that* as my stepsister?'

'Not another word!' Now Gerald's voice was bitingly cold. 'I regret having told you of my intentions, Declan. I didn't dream you would react in this way.'

'No?'

'No. And all this when I haven't even asked Brenda. She might not accept my proposal after all.'

'Oh, she'll accept, all right,' the hard voice said bitterly. 'In fact, she'll bite your hand off. I should think the lady won't believe her luck.'

'I'm not listening to any more of this,' Gerald said furiously. 'I'm going to ask her to marry me and that's that. And if you can't accept her into the family then I suggest you make yourself scarce, boy. I won't have her upset in any way.'

'I'll do just that!' Declan growled angrily. 'Don't worry, Father, I'll keep my distance from now on. I don't particularly want to see the mess you're going to make of your life anyway.'

Paige had found her legs at that point, flying up the long winding staircase to her room and locking the door behind her before collapsing on the bed in an agony of helpless outrage and burning, blinding pain. He thought her mother was a gold-digger, one of those avaricious, grasping women who would marry purely to secure themselves a fat bank balance and luxurious lifestyle! Her mother! Her sweet, unworldly, gentle mother! She pounded the bed with her fists, her eyes dry and burning, her pain too intense for tears. How dared he? *How dared he*? There wasn't a trace of any of those characteristics in her mother's make-up, in fact just the opposite. If anything she was too generous, too giving, always ready with a free meal or a sub to a friend even when they were having a job to make ends meet themselves. The swine! The cruel, cold-blooded swine!

Her brain refused to dwell on the brutal comment about herself but later, when they arrived home after all the excitement of the wedding announcement, her mother bright-eyed and flushed with happiness, she went to her small box-room as soon as she could and lay in the darkness with her heart breaking. 'That awful daughter.' The harsh, condemning words rang in her ears now all was quiet. 'Do you seriously expect me to acknowledge *that* as my stepsister?' She couldn't bear it, she just couldn't bear it. She knew she was plain, under-sized for her age, but, surrounded as she had always been by her mother's love and several good friends, it hadn't mattered too much, or she had tried not to let it. But now all the kindness was ripped aside and she saw herself for exactly what she was. Ugly, totally unprepossessing, something a man would pity or worse.

The intense irrationality of the young was working overtime but she was too distraught to curb her illogical thoughts; suddenly she was the most revolting thing on two legs and it hurt, shockingly.

It was a long, dark night and she didn't close her eyes once during it, but by the time the night sky had given way before the tentative fingers of dawn she had left her childhood behind forever, and reached several irrevocable decisions.

Firstly, she would not tell her mother anything of what she had overheard. If Brenda thought she was the instrument in forcing a wedge between Gerald and his son she could quite easily break the engagement in spite of being head over heels in love with her fiancé, besides which, Declan's opinion of her would hurt her mother dreadfully. No, she must keep it to herself.

Secondly, she would take her A levels and go on to college; try for that fashion course that was so sought after. She had been undecided for weeks about furthering her education, especially after enquiring after the course she had in mind and discovering the high standard of A level passes needed to even be eligible for consideration. There were two hundred and fifty applicants for every place, she had been told by a very superior careers officer, who had looked askance at her childish shape in the unflattering school uniform, the severe hairstyle and thick metal brace. Well, she would work every second of the day and night for the next two years and try for a place. She *would*.

Thirdly, she would ask her mother to buy her contact lenses for her birthday, get her hair cut in a more flattering style, and be diligent in applying the cream the doctor had given her for her skin. 'Just a temporary thing,' he had assured her at the time, 'growing up and all that. Use this cream for a few months and the spots will go.'

And fourthly, but most important of all, she would get even with Declan if it was the last thing she ever did. She would make him eat every cruel, heartless word one day and revel in it. Yes, she *would*. And so her future had been shaped on a conversation overheard one sunny June day.

Paige came back to the present with a little start of annoyance. She couldn't afford to daydream today of all days; she had to finish these sketches and get them to the office before she left for the country tomorrow. She had got four A-grade passes in her A levels and the college had snapped her up at the interview when they had seen her exquisite artwork and portfolio full of original ideas. She had enjoyed her three years there and the icing on the cake had been the fabulous commission on graduation day from a top manufacturer who had seen her work on display and liked it.

'Come on, Paige, *work*,' she told herself firmly after glancing in happy approval round the bright living-room of her tiny flat. She adjusted the lamp on top of her large drawing-board, spread out her sketches on the long coffee-table by her stool, and applied herself to the task in hand.

She had gone on from strength to strength with the firm who had employed her when she had left college twelve months ago, but was wise enough to understand that she was still very much a junior designer, capable of all the mistakes that only experience could erase. But to date they had loved her work and she was thoroughly enjoying her latest theme, a range of exclusive and wildly expensive clothing for evening wear. She glanced at a few of the samples of material at her feet. Raw silk, pure bleached linen and heavily embroidered cotton in dazzling colours. Her idea was to combine the different materials, but she needed to tread carefully. It was all very well being a frontier-breaker but only if the rich and often very bored women whom she targeted for her designs approved. Too often they were like indolent spoilt cats, ever ready to unsheath their claws and verbally rip hard-won careers apart.

As the phone interrupted her thought-flow again she sighed softly, reaching out for it with an irritable hand and speaking her number into the receiver.

'Paige? It's me, sorry. Were you working?'

'Of course I was working, Matthew, what else would I be doing at half-past ten on a Thursday morning?' she said patiently.

'Yes, well, sorry,' the voice apologised again and she grimaced in exasperation. Why was Matthew always so nice? she thought testily. Why did he seem to make a positive *career* of it? She felt immediately contrite at the unfairness of the thought and forced more warmth into her voice when she next spoke.

'Sorry, Matthew. I didn't mean to put you down, but I've masses to do...so?' She waited a second. 'Why have you rung?' she asked more sharply. 'I'll be in the office later.'

'Just to say I might be a bit delayed tomorrow.' Matthew's voice held that note of worried concern that was habitual with him. 'Would your mother mind if we were a little late—say, eightish?'

'Not at all,' Paige said shortly. 'I'll ring her later and let her know. Goodbye, then.' She had put down the phone before he could reply—Matthew was apt to waffle on all day. A son of one of the partners in the firm she worked for, he was a hard worker when he didn't really have to be, quiet and pleasant with everyone, even when they took gross liberties, and altogether one of the nicest people she had ever met. Blond good looks and a wealthy father hadn't spoilt him an iota and she always enjoyed her dates with him, and yet... She sighed to herself as she resumed work at the drawing-board. There was something missing, some...spark. She shook herself angrily. What was the matter with her today? It was the thought of seeing Declan tomorrow. That was enough to put anyone in a bad humour.

She had only met him three times since that first fateful encounter, and all within months of each other. First at her mother's wedding six weeks after the barbecue party, when he had been grim and silent and she had patently ignored him. Then that first Christmas when he had called briefly on Christmas Eve with an armful of presents and a tight face, staying just an hour and quite ruining everyone's Christmas as his unseen presence had brooded over the following days. And then a few weeks into the New Year when Gerald had called him down specially from London. She didn't know what had been said on that occasion but she hadn't seen him again during the time she still lived with her mother and Gerald. She had moved into a shared flat when she was at college and had rarely visited the huge old house in the country, mainly because she was worried she might run into Declan, although she understood from her mother during a recent conversation that it was only in the last few months that father and son had communicated at all.

There was a definite bite to the cool evening air as Matthew's BMW drew up outside Gerald's house just after eight the next night. As Paige unfolded herself from the car, Matthew's hand at her elbow, she stretched gracefully. It had been a long drive but the powerful, comfortable car had made it pleasurable, or would have if she had only been able to control the sick churning in her stomach, she corrected mentally. The long drive was packed with cars of every description but one stood out from all the rest immediately. A long, low, sleek silver monster on wheels that crouched broodingly under a huge oak tree looking for all the world as if it was preparing to pounce any moment.

'Wow!' Matthew's eyes were fixed longingly on the car as she glanced at him. 'Who do you suppose owns that beauty?'

'Someone with more money than sense, I should think,' Paige said practically. 'The insurance alone must cost a fortune!'

'Maybe it's an old-age pensioner who gets an "over sixties" discount,' Matthew said wryly. 'I never think it's fair that you have to be in your dotage before you can enjoy having a sports car like that!'

'Your eyes are turning green,' Paige said reprovingly as they walked arm in arm up the old stone steps

to the front door, suddenly immensely glad of his un-
complicated friendship as he rang the bell, smiling up
gratefully into his face as the door swung open in
answer to their arrival.

As she glanced from the man at her side to the tall,
dark figure in front of them she was conscious of the
world standing still for a split-second and then roaring
on at twice the normal speed, the noise of the party
only faintly registering on her stunned senses.

'Good evening.' Declan held out his hand and Paige
took it mechanically, almost recoiling as she felt the
hard, warm flesh enfolding hers. 'I don't think we've
met.' She was immensely thankful when he let go of
her hand and shook Matthew's, drawing them both
into the hall as he stepped backwards. 'I'm Declan,
Gerald's son, by the way.'

'How do you do,' Matthew answered for both of
them; she was quite beyond speech, although her face
portrayed none of the inner turmoil that was tightening her stomach into a giant knot. She knew
Matthew was waiting for her to make some comment,
to explain this strange situation that had his brows
creasing in a frown. She had told him Gerald had a
son but that was all, and it was obvious he found the
apparent lack of recognition between Declan and
herself astounding.

'Come on, Matthew.' She kept her arm locked in
his as she drew him towards the drawing-room, totally
ignoring Declan as though he didn't exist, although
she was vitally aware of the startling stiffening of the
big body at such blatant rudeness. The swift appraisal
she had made before she had dropped her eyes had

told her Declan was subtly different from the brash young man she remembered. The square face was even harder than she recalled and there was a surprising sprinkling of silver in the springy black hair that made the silver-grey eyes all the more startling. The aura that surrounded him was one of dark, controlled force and she shivered against its insidious intrusion into her hard-won independent identity. What was the matter with her? she thought irritably. She was used to dealing with all sorts of men in the cut-and-thrust challenge of the fashion world. She couldn't let a rat like him affect her.

'Paige?' Matthew was looking down at her with troubled eyes. 'I don't understand. That was your stepbrother, wasn't it? Doesn't——?'

'Please, Matthew.' She saw her mother approaching from the other side of the room at the same time as being aware of a tall dark shadow standing just inside the doorway. The moment of reckoning had come. What would he think of the 'awful' little schoolgirl now? 'I'll explain it all later.'

'Paige, darling...' Her mother swooped on her with an exclamation of delight, hugging her close for a second before pushing her away to examine her more closely. 'You look absolutely gorgeous, doesn't she, Declan?' She had known he would move to their side when he heard her name and she forced her eyes away from her mother's bright face to meet the hard, penetrating stare that was boring into her brain.

'Paige?' The moment was sweet and she savoured it with all her might. 'You're little Paige?' The silver eyes were narrowed in disbelieving wonder as they swept over the slender, full-breasted figure, smooth-skinned and long-legged with a mass of warm chestnut-red hair framing a heart-shaped face in which huge hazel eyes were set like jewels in a crown. She had designed her dress and jacket herself and knew the rich silk in a soft clinging cream suited her skin and hair to perfection, the soft folds of the material clinging to her womanly shape in a manner guaranteed to turn even the most jaded male eye.

The hated brace had assured a twenty-four-carat smile that she now switched on to automatic as she steeled herself to hold his eyes. 'Of course I'm Paige,' she said coolly with just the right amount of disdain to show him she was not impressed. 'What did you expect? A brace and ponytail? I left those *awful* things behind some years ago.' She let the smile fade slowly.

There was no trace of understanding in the piercing eyes watching her so closely. He clearly didn't remember his words of so long ago, and why should he? Paige thought bitterly as she maintained her ice-cool front. The careless cruelty that had stabbed her soul so savagely was just part and parcel of this man. He would break a fellow human being without a second thought if it suited his purpose. Why *should* he remember the brutal words he had spoken six years ago about a plain little schoolgirl and her mother? But she remembered. And he would pay.

'I wouldn't have recognised you—I *didn't* recognise you!' the deep voice said wryly. 'I think I've been very remiss in not renewing the acquaintance of my little stepsister before now.' He smiled briefly at Matthew, who was watching the proceedings with unconcealed interest and faint unease. 'We haven't met for years,' he explained unnecessarily.

'Remiss? I don't think so,' she said coldly. 'We aren't related, after all, and I'm sure we have nothing in common.' She turned away in deliberate dismissal and took her mother's arm as she slipped her hand in Matthew's, effectively shutting Declan out of the charmed circle. 'Where's Gerald?' she asked flatly as she drew the other two further into the room.

'Paige! That was very rude,' her mother whispered nervously with an uneasy glance over her shoulder.

'Leave it, Mum, please.' Paige softened her words with a little smile as she touched her mother's worried face gently. 'I promise to be a good girl now that's over, OK? He had it coming after all, ignoring us all for years and then acting as though he's my long-lost brother.'

'I don't think it was brotherly emotion that was prompting that interest,' Matthew said drily by her side, and as she raised startled eyes to his mild blue ones she saw they were shadowed with concern. 'Care to tell me what that was all about?'

'Later.' She waved her hand distractedly. 'Here's Gerald.'

The evening rolled smoothly on, the careful timing of the buffet, dancing to the little band ensconced in the large bay of the vast sun-room leading off the drawing-room, and general flawless organisation convincing Paige that a brain other than her mother's had overseen the proceedings. She loved her mother dearly but would have been the first to admit that Brenda's innate helplessness was part of her charm.

She caught sight of Declan's dark figure once or twice but turned away immediately, annoyed at the fluttering in her stomach that his presence induced. He approached her once as the band began to play, asking her to dance with a polite nod at Matthew sitting by her side, his smile fading as she stiffly refused.

'Paige, what *is* the matter with you?' Matthew asked as the tall figure disappeared back into the crowd. 'I've never seen you like this before. He is your step-brother, after all.'

'I know, Matthew, I know,' she replied quietly, sighing as her pulse-rate returned to normal. 'We just don't get on, that's all. Please...' She knew she was behaving badly but there was a strange fluttering excitement warming her blood that had nothing to do with the wine she had consumed. There was something about Declan, a dark, controlled maleness, that set her nerves on edge to the point where the need to freeze him out, to utterly scorn him, had become of paramount importance. He was so self-assured, so cool, so very much the aloof spectator watching the common herd enjoying themselves that her senses were screaming in protest. How could she explain that to Matthew?

She glanced across the room now in the direction he had gone and was suddenly transfixed as she met the silver-grey gaze head-on. He was standing leaning against the far wall, wine glass in hand and big body relaxed, his face unsmiling and the piercing eyes fixed on her face. For a brief second of time she held his gaze, her wide hazel eyes revealing her opinion of him far more adequately than words, and then she wrenched her glance away with a feeling of panic clawing at her throat. Within seconds her view had been obstructed by gaily dancing couples, but as she sank back in her seat it was as though some form of physical contact had been made and she was shaking from the shock of it.

'Are you all right?' Matthew said at her shoulder. 'You haven't been yourself all evening and you're as white as a sheet. You're not sickening for something, are you?'

'Maybe,' Paige said wearily without elaborating on the fact that the only virus affecting her was a distinctly distasteful one called Declan. 'It's been a long day.'

'Paige?' Matthew touched her gently on the arm as his other hand turned her chin round so he could look into her eyes. 'I thought we were friends? Nothing heavy, OK, but good old-fashioned friends who could talk to each other. But you aren't talking, Paige, and I know there's something badly wrong. Can't you share it with me?'

'If I could talk to anyone it would be you, Matt,' Paige said quietly as the sudden rush of tears into the back of her eyes made her hands clench in protest. What was the matter with her, for goodness' sake? She was acting like a child. 'But it's something I thought I was over and it would appear I'm not. Maybe some day, yes?' She smiled into his troubled face. 'I'd love a coffee.'

'Won't be a tick.' As he disappeared through to the dining-room on the other side of the house she leant back in her seat with a small sigh. The warm, heavy air impregnated with expensive perfume and cigar smoke competed with the scent of hothouse flowers and suddenly it was too much. Without thinking she rose from her seat, walking across the room and through the archway into the sun-room, making for the wide open glass doors that overlooked the beautifully landscaped garden. There was a long wooden bench just to one side of the doors and she sank on to it gratefully, lifting her face to the cool breeze that teased her hair into.glowing tendrils round her flushed cheeks. Matthew would find her here; she hadn't gone far. She shut her eyes for a moment; all this nervous excitement was somewhat wearing on the system, she reflected ruefully.

'Alone at last.' The deep sardonic voice right in her ear brought her eyes wide open at the same time as Declan lowered himself on to the seat beside her, stretching out his long legs with a small sigh as he rested a casual arm along the back of the bench behind her shoulders. Nerves she had never known she possessed leapt into life at his closeness; she had never dreamt it was possible to react so violently to another human being.

'What do you want?' she asked faintly as the full force of the steel-hard gaze sliced into her at close range, causing a physical jolt in her chest.

'What do I want?' His tone was slightly mocking and very dry, the dark dinner-suit and snowy white shirt he was wearing turning him into a vivid black and white picture in which colour had no part. 'I want to talk to you. Is that permissible?'

'No! Yes, I mean . . .' Her voice trailed away as he gave a slow, amused chuckle, the sound curling her toes inwards. 'What I mean is, I'm waiting for Matthew,' she said weakly, hearing herself with a shaft of self-disgust that put fire in her cheeks. 'He's bringing me coffee, so I can't——' Her voice stopped abruptly as he reached out a hand and touched the heavy fall of red silky hair that was resting on her shoulders.

'Beautiful, quite beautiful,' he said softly, his eyes wickedly sensual as they came to rest on her half-open mouth. 'Close to, there is such a combination of colour in your hair that I wouldn't know how to determine the shade.'

'It's chestnut,' she said tightly, forcing the panic that was clawing at her throat into submission. 'And it's natural, in case you were going to ask.' Her chin raised a fraction.

'I wouldn't dream of presuming in such a way.' There was a thread of laughter in his voice that jarred painfully. He clearly found her most amusing, she thought angrily, the idea causing her hazel eyes to darken into jade-green. 'And any fool can see that it's natural, along with that flawless skin and certain other attributes that add up to a quite delicious whole.' The lazy voice was irritatingly confident.

As a line it was pretty good, she thought balefully as she found her voice along with her wits. How many other women did he sweet-talk so outrageously? 'I'm glad you approve,' she said coolly as she stood up in one graceful movement, her eyes as cold as ice. 'Now, if you'll excuse me . . .'

'Not before you've answered something that's been bothering me all night,' he said softly as he reached out an authoritative hand and jerked her back down beside him before she realised what he had done. She glared at him angrily as she caught her breath. How dared he manhandle her? *How dared he*?

'Do you mind?' she said furiously with a look that could have speared a fish at fifty yards. He smiled coldly.

'I don't but you do, and that's what I want to ask you about.' He shifted slightly in his seat and as he did so she became aware of the leashed strength in the big body so close to hers. The wide powerful shoulders and broad chest were more in keeping with an athlete than a businessman, she thought faintly, and the dark, rugged face was faintly piratical. Not handsome, not even attractive in the traditional sense of conventional good looks, but there was something...a magnetism, something almost hypnotic in the harsh, proud face that was powerfully seductive. She had never been in the presence of such charisma before and she didn't like it! She took a long hidden breath. She didn't like it at all.

'Well?' She raised her chin as her wide hazel eyes met the silver-grey of his. 'What is it?' She blessed the control that was keeping her back straight and her head high when she felt like melting into a little pool at his feet and trickling silently away out of sight.

'To my knowledge we have only met three times, maybe four, in our entire lives,' he said softly, his deep, slightly gravelly voice thoughtful. 'I certainly don't remember exchanging more than a dozen words with you in that time, and yet...' he stared at her keenly as though he would look into her mind '...you clearly dislike me, have displayed extreme rudeness and antagonism from the first moment we met to-night, and I want to know why.' There was a hard smile touching the edge of his mouth as he spoke. 'I would expect such behaviour from a scorned lover or piqued sweetheart, but you... It doesn't add up.'

'It doesn't add up?' She smiled coldly as a shiver of wind stroked a few red silky strands of hair across her cheek. 'And everything adds up in your world? Always?'

'Maybe not, but don't change the subject,' he said coolly. 'I can't believe you are the hard, cold woman I see in front of me now. Those warm, full lips and wonderful hair speak of passion, fire, heat... Am I wrong?'

'Quite wrong.' She eyed him furiously. 'And why should I bother to acknowledge our tenuous relationship anyway? Your father happened to marry my mother when I was sixteen and you were already an adult. We don't know each other, to my knowledge you haven't bothered with either your father or the rest of the family for years; I don't know you from Adam!'

'That could be easily rectified,' he said mockingly as his eyes wandered purposefully over her face, dwelling for a moment on the softness of her lower lip before returning to meet the huge, thickly lashed eyes sparking with anger. 'I think maybe I would like to get to know my little stepsister.'

'Well, your "little stepsister" doesn't want to get to know *you*,' she said sharply, the long-awaited victory of the moment utterly spoilt by the trembling that was threatening to communicate itself through her limbs. 'And you are quite right, I do dislike you! I dislike you very much indeed.'

The abruptness with which he moved caught her totally by surprise, and as she felt his firm, hard lips stroke her mouth fleetingly her senses caught a whiff of deliciously male aftershave, lemony and sharp, and then he had stood up, his mouth smiling but his eyes as cold as ice. 'Now that's a shame, Paige.' There was no humour in the smile and she felt a little trickle of apprehension flicker down her spine at the controlled menace in his dark face. 'But perhaps you'll change your mind.'

'I wouldn't bank on it,' she said determinedly. 'If that's what you're hoping for, you——'

'I'm not in the habit of "hoping" for anything,' he broke in smoothly. 'I leave that sort of emotion to the poets and philosophers. When I want something I make sure I get it. It's as simple as that.' She wasn't aware of her hand moving to her lips where the touch of his mouth was burning like fire, but as his eyes followed the action it registered on her bruised senses and she brought her hand down with a jerking snap, lowering her eyes in the same instant. The man was a monster!

He was standing arrogantly in front of her, the outline of his muscular thighs on a level with her eyeline, and as she still kept her head lowered to avoid him reading the confusion and fear in her eyes she heard him laugh softly, the sound gratingly harsh. 'But maybe I don't want you, Paige; you'll just have to "hope" for the best, won't you?'

The mockery was too much and she reared up like a scalded cat, the bright colour in her cheeks on a par with her hair. 'I don't "hope" for anything either, as it happens,' she spat bitterly. 'What I want I work for, and what I *don't* want I make sure doesn't happen, regardless of any Tom, Dick or Harry who might think otherwise!' The venom in her tone was caustically savage. 'You don't impress me with your clever little speeches and veiled threats, so don't think you do. Your type are ten a penny and just as cheap. Goodbye, Declan.'

This time she took him by surprise, swinging on her heel with a lightning movement and striding off through the open doors into the bright lights without a backward glance. She was shaking with rage and a mixture of other emotions that she couldn't have put a name to, and as she saw Matthew in the distance standing to one side of the main throng with two cups of coffee in his hands she felt a rush of affection for the tall, very English figure that made her reach up and kiss his cheek as she arrived at his side, knowing he wouldn't mistake the friendly gesture for anything other than what it was.

'OK, sweetheart?' He smiled down at her slowly. 'Drink that and then I'll have to be going. There's a meeting with the Thailand suppliers tomorrow and Dad wants me to get some figures ready so he can glance over them before they arrive. You're back on Monday, aren't you?'

'Yes.' She nodded as she took the proffered coffee. 'I thought I'd stay the weekend with Mum, but...' Her voice dwindled away. 'I might come back early.'

It was as she raised the cup to her lips that she saw Declan watching a few feet away, his eyes dancing with mockery and his face sardonic. It was obvious he had heard their conversation, that he had been listening, he was making no attempt to pretend otherwise; and it was equally obvious that her scathing snub of a few minutes before had had no effect at all on his monstrous ego. She bit her lower lip until it hurt in an effort to betray none of the murderous rage that his cool cruel face inspired in her and then deliberately turned her back on him, her head high.

She *would* stay the weekend now. She didn't know if he would be around but if he was it would make no difference at all. She wouldn't skulk off back to the city as though his presence bothered her; in fact she would make sure he knew she didn't care enough about him to even be aware of whether he was there or not. She didn't dislike him any more, she *hated* him! Totally, utterly, completely, and she would have her day with this man! She nodded a mental promise to herself. If it was the last thing she did, if it took years, she would bring Declan Stone to his knees.

CHAPTER TWO

As SHE waved Matthew off into the darkness from the top of the steps Paige sensed, rather than heard, the body behind her and tensed immediately. It was Declan. It *had* to be Declan.

'Isn't lover-boy staying the night?' the hated voice drawled slowly behind her as the tail-lights of Matthew's car were lost to sight in the velvet blackness. 'What could entice him away from your side and possibly... your bed?'

She swung round in an instant with her hand raised, but he had anticipated her reaction and caught her arm easily, his face still and watchful in the dim light from the half-open door. 'Now, now, now...' he said softly. 'Is that the way to treat your elders?' His eyes laughed at her angry face.

'Let go of me,' she snapped quietly, her eyes shooting daggers at the big broad figure in front of her.

'Are you going to behave yourself if I do?' he asked tauntingly. 'It wouldn't do for Brenda or Father to have their evening ruined because their children were fighting, would it?' The silver eyes roamed over her hot flesh. 'Have you considered that aspect in this ridiculous vendetta you seem to have against me?' His smile was cool and without warmth.

'I can be civil in front of them if I have to,' she said tightly, struggling to free her arm from his iron fist and then relaxing wearily as she realised he wouldn't release her until he was ready to do so.

'And if I don't play ball?' he asked scornfully. 'Maybe I would object to such hypocrisy? You may live your life on such a regrettable level but I don't like insincerity.'

'Not even if it protects people you love?' she asked flatly as he let her arm drop to her side.

'Not even then.' As she looked up at him she was aware of thinking, inconsequentially, that he wasn't as tall as she had first thought. Five feet eleven, six feet maybe, but he gave the impression of being much taller, although she couldn't have explained why. Perhaps it was the hard-muscled bulk of him, the austere, compelling face with its magnetic attraction—whatever, he gave the feeling of menacing strength that was as uncomfortable as it was unnerving. 'If you expect me to go along with this little charade then I shall expect politeness at all times, Paige. Do you understand me?' There was no vestige of amusement or mockery in his face now, he was deadly serious. 'I do not play games, I am too old for such trivia. You toe the line with me or take the consequences.' He eyed her coldly.

She would have loved to snap back with a sharp comment but there was something in the hard face that stopped her. She suddenly knew, with absolute conviction, that here was a man who did not make idle threats and, much as it infuriated her, he was holding all the aces. She *didn't* want her mother and Gerald upset and he knew it. How she hated him!

'How long are you staying?' she prevaricated, and again that humourless smile touched the edge of his mouth.

'Do I take that as agreement?' he asked softly. 'Agreement that you will act in a reasonable manner with or without an audience?' She stared at him angrily and he shook his head slowly as real amusement filtered into the silvery eyes. 'You intrigue me, Miss Paige Stone,' he began lightly, his expression hardening as she leapt away from him as though she had been burnt, her face indignant even as it whitened in protest.

'My name is Paige *Green*,' she said sharply, 'not Stone. I chose to keep my father's name when Mum married Gerald, although that is no reflection on your father. I like him very much, but as far as I'm concerned he married Mum, not me.' Her voice was bitterly fierce.

'And exactly what does that mean?' Declan asked quietly as he stepped back a pace, crossing his arms as he closed the door behind him and leant against it, his bulk dark against the light wood and his hard face imperturbable.

She shivered in the cold night air and considered requesting admission to the house, then decided against it. She might as well see this thing through right now and let him know what she thought of him—but not the reason for it, never that. That would be a humiliation that would be too great to bear. Those cruel words so casually spoken years ago had reached through and pierced the very core of her and she could never give him the satisfaction of knowing how much they had hurt. That night was a secret she would take with her to the grave. She had a lot to thank him for really, she thought bitterly. Knowing herself as she did, she had to admit she would never have had the motivation to succeed so steadfastly without the memory of that dark, scornful voice to goad her on.

'It means that you are your father's son as I am my mother's daughter,' she said softly. 'Your father is enormously wealthy, and when he married Mum we had next to nothing, as I'm sure you're aware.' The implacable face stiffened slightly but otherwise showed no emotion at all. 'I am very grateful for all the kindness Gerald has shown me, but now I'm independent, and if anything should happen to either of them I don't want a penny of your father's money.'

'Are you serious?' he asked grimly. 'Have you told my father this?' His eyes raked her face, seeking the truth.

'Of course.' She raised her head jerkily. 'He wouldn't accept it at first, but then I reiterated my feelings when I was twenty-one and he promised me that they would be respected. I don't need your family's money, Declan, and I don't want it.' She stared him straight in the eye, her face painfully proud.

'You must have hurt him,' he said, almost condemningly.

She stared at him in surprise. It wasn't the reaction she had expected, but then, she acknowledged silently, she hadn't known what to expect. 'I think it did at first, until I made him understand that it didn't affect what I felt for him as a person,' she said slowly. 'I like—no, love your father, Declan. He's as different from you as chalk from cheese.'

'I can buy that,' he said unemotionally. 'Why do you feel so strongly about all this, Paige? There must be a reason.'

'That's my own business,' she said stonily as her eyes flashed.

'And one you have no intention of telling me.' It was a terse statement. 'The same as you don't intend to reveal why you dislike me so strongly?' She nodded her answer and the tough face nodded with her. 'You're quite a mystery girl, Paige *Green*.' His eyes narrowed on the lovely face in front of him. 'And in spite of what you may think, I don't indulge in social flattery. When I said I thought you were beautiful I meant it. Can you accept that?'

She shrugged slowly. 'It doesn't matter one way or the other, does it?' She forced her voice to be cool although there was a trembling taking hold of her limbs that was unnerving. It was his closeness. She stared at him as he leaned nonchalantly against the door. He was so vitally male, so very different. She had never felt the power of such blatant sensuality before and yet it was an integral part of this man. He had had it at twenty-four when she had first seen him and it had grown dangerously with the intervening years. He would attract women without trying. It wasn't his looks, it wasn't even his body; she didn't know what it was. A combination of everything, probably, but whatever, it was terrifying at this close range.

'Are you frightened of me?' he asked abruptly as he straightened away from the building and took a step towards her.

'Of course not,' she said tightly, but then as he took another step nearer her legs backed away in spite of herself.

'You are, aren't you?' he muttered incredulously as his eyes raked over her white face. 'What the hell...?' His voice died away as he ran a furious hand through the thick shock of black hair edged with silver. 'Who on earth has been feeding you stories about me?' He was by her side now and she steeled herself not to retreat any further as he stared down at her, his eyes dark with angry puzzlement. 'What have you heard?'

You'd be amazed at what I heard, she thought bitterly. She couldn't believe he was Gerald's son. She could see nothing of the reserved, aristocratic man she thought of as a dear friend in this fierce individual in front of her. 'I haven't heard anything.' She raised her chin slightly to combat the shivering in her stomach. He was so close that she could see the long, curling eyelashes that should have been quite out of place on such a hard-planed face but instead gave it a subtle sensuality that was stunning and incredibly attractive.

'No?' It was obvious he didn't believe her.

'What is there to hear?' she said tightly, forcing a thread of ridicule into her voice. It didn't quite come off and the narrowed eyes were both perceptive and mocking.

'Oh, the usual things...' She had known he was going to kiss her again but had been powerless to stop it happening, and now as his mouth closed down on hers she found herself drawn into his arms and held tightly against the hard body as his lips plundered hers. He certainly knew how to kiss, she thought faintly as she felt her senses begin to swim, and she couldn't, *mustn't* respond. She ought to be struggling, she ought... but instead of all the things she ought to be doing she found herself kissing him back. There was a mastery, a deep sensual warmth in his lovemaking that was frighteningly powerful, and even as she told herself he was devastatingly experienced, that he'd done this a thousand times before, she felt herself responding to this thing she had felt from the first moment she had seen him at sixteen, before the hurt had burnt it away.

He raised his head to look at her after a long moment, loosening his hold on her body, a look of strain about his mouth. 'Paige?' His voice was hoarse and he shook his head dazedly, the look in his eyes mirrored in her own as he pulled her back against him more roughly now, seeking her mouth with an urgency that frightened her even as it thrilled. Suddenly the kiss was subtly different from anything she had ever known before, and as his hands stroked down her slender shape, moulding her curves against his hardness in sensual familiarity, cold reason returned in an icy deluge.

'Stop, please stop...' She jerked herself out of his hold with a violence that almost made her fall, backing away from him as though he were the devil himself. He made no attempt to follow her; indeed he seemed turned to stone, and as she opened the front door and stumbled through he was still standing on the second step, his face taut and his eyes bleak, his hands thrust deep into his pockets.

She found her mother in the middle of a laughing group listening to one of Gerald's endless jokes, and after pleading a migraine escaped to her room, stripping off her clothes as she paced the floor and standing under the shower for long minutes until her heartbeat returned to normal and the pink flush staining her skin drained away.

How could I have let him kiss me like that? she thought agitatedly. After all she'd said, all the fine words and cold reasoning, to fall into his arms so wantonly... He knew she didn't like him, knew she despised him; what must he be thinking now? She ground her teeth in an agony of helpless frustration as the water continued to rain down on her bent head, lifting her face after a time for the needle-sharp drops to mingle with her tears of rage and confusion.

She just couldn't *believe* she'd acted like that! It cut through everything she knew about herself. 'It was the wine,' she whispered to herself later as she lay curled on the large double bed in the beautiful room that had been hers until she had left for college four years ago. 'The wine and the shock of seeing him again and tiredness and...' She ran out of excuses.

How he would be laughing at her! The thought drove her nails into the palms of her hands in helpless rage. 'Well, I won't give him the chance to make a fool of me again,' she declared to the empty room as she slipped under the fresh cotton sheets. From now on she would be icily polite and nothing else. No con-

frontations, no gibes, no further revelations and certainly—she closed her eyes for a second—certainly no
more kisses.

She woke very early the next morning after just a few
hours' sleep and lay watching the night sky change to
the soft mauves and blues that heralded a new day,
opening her window after a time and drinking in the
soft country air, the pure tranquil peacefulness of the
sleeping garden giving a timelessness to the morning
that was a balm to her sore heart.

  By the time she went down to breakfast two hours
later she was, outwardly at least, the epitome of the
cool, calm Englishwoman at home in the country. Her
thick shoulder-length hair was secured in a shining
ponytail at the back of her head, her figure was
encased in heavy cream linen trousers and matching
open-necked shirt and her feet shod in smart, sensible
brogues.

  'Morning.' Gerald was sitting in solitary splendour
in the large breakfast-room as she entered, the sun-
light streaming through the window behind him and
turning his grey head into a crown of white. 'How
did you sleep?'

  'Fine, thanks,' she lied smilingly. 'All alone?'

  'Your mother never rises before ten, as you know,'
he said with a little frown of disapproval. Gerald was
one of the old school who insisted on a full cooked
breakfast at seven sharp every morning come hell or
high water. He had never been able to understand her
mother's weakness for late mornings, but indulged
her reasonably cheerfully, with just the odd reproving

remark now and again. They were still so much in love, Paige thought enviously, as she helped herself to scrambled eggs and bacon from the covered dishes on the trolley at the side of the table, after thanking Millicent, Gerald's diamond of a housekeeper, for the fresh toast she brought through as soon as she heard Paige's voice.

'I was surprised to see Declan home,' she said carefully after they had eaten in companionable silence for some minutes. 'Do I take it things have improved between you two?'

Gerald nodded quickly, and Paige was touched to see his reserved face soften as he thought of his only son. 'I've your mother to thank for it all really,' he said quietly. 'She contacted Declan and asked him to meet her in London a few days ago and had a little heart-to-heart with him. I don't know what was said, I only found out about it by chance last night by something Declan said, but he came extending the olive-branch, which I must admit I was only too pleased to accept. I've missed him, Paige.' He looked at her almost shamefacedly. 'Does that sound weak?'

'It sounds perfectly normal to me,' Paige said stoutly. 'He's your son, for goodness' sake, Gerald. It's only natural you should want him around.'

'I have to confess I've never understood him,' her stepfather said thoughtfully. 'His mother did, perfectly, and they were very close. Still, that's often the way, I guess. Sons and mothers, fathers and daughters.'

'Yes.' She smiled carefully even as her heart reached out to him at his obvious disappointment. How could

Declan have shut him out for years? It was utterly heartless.

Her pulse leapt violently as the door opened and the object of her wrath entered, the blood pounding in her ears for a moment as though she had run a twenty-mile race.

'Father. Paige.' Declan nodded to them both with a small smile and Paige forced her suddenly stiff lips to respond in like as she mumbled a reply. The rugged, harsh face was quite distant and remote as he glanced at her, but she found him as completely devastating in the cold light of day as she had last night, more so if anything.

The loose-fitting grey trousers and light blue silk shirt sat on the big body easily, the open collar revealing a few inches of tanned hair-covered chest that made her breath catch suddenly in her throat. It was almost as if he was thrusting his masculinity at her, forcing her to acknowledge his vigour, and although she knew it was totally unfair her hackles rose at his presence. She had never been particularly attracted to blatantly virile men, preferring brains to brawn, but, knowing what she did about Declan's successful career, it was clear he had a good supply of both! The light touch of silver at his temples added to, rather than detracted from, his dangerously intriguing appeal, and as he sat down at the table she knew he was aware of the confusion in her glance by the way the grey eyes had narrowed.

'I hope you slept well?' She nodded a reply as she quickly averted her gaze. 'I hope you slept well'. Perfectly innocent words in themselves, but she just knew he was mocking her again. He knew how he had affected her last night and was enjoying every moment of her discomfiture this morning. How very like him!

'Paige?' She came to, to find Gerald smiling at her with the paternal amusement he kept just for her. 'I asked you if you'd got any plans for today?' he repeated indulgently.

'Sorry.' She returned the smile as her cheeks turned pink and kept her gaze away from the big dark figure opposite. 'I was daydreaming. I thought I'd perhaps go into town and have a wander round the shops, maybe go for a drive in the country if I can borrow one of the cars?'

'No need.' Declan's deep, husky voice broke into the conversation. 'I'm here until the weekend. I'll take you.'

'No!' The word had shot out before she had time to hold it back and she saw Gerald stiffen out of the corner of her eye. Damn, damn, damn! Careful, Paige, she thought silently. 'No, you don't have to do that,' she hedged quickly. 'I haven't met a man yet who likes shopping, and I tend to dither about all day, I'm afraid. I wouldn't dream——'

'I said I'll take you.' He raised his eyes from his plate as he spoke and the result was electrifying. She found it quite impossible to look away, to break the piercing silver light. 'It's settled.' His face was as hard as granite.

'Oh.' She heard the murmur with a heavy dose of self-disgust but realised she had been out-manoeuvred by an expert. All she could do now was to accept as naturally as she could for Gerald's benefit. 'Well, that's really kind of you, Declan,' she said prettily as her brain clicked into action. 'I do hope you won't be too bored.' Two can play at this game, she thought determinedly. 'It will be so nice to get to know each other after all this time, won't it?' She saw Gerald relax in the background.

'My thoughts exactly.' There was a wicked innuendo in the softly drawled words that was just for her ears alone, and as the grey eyes lingered for an infinitesimal moment on her lips she had the mad impulse to reach up her hand and scrub at them with her napkin. It was just as though he had kissed her again, and she found her whole body responding in spite of her rage.

Gerald sat in happy contentment, totally oblivious to the undercurrents that were swirling in full force about him. His mild gaze reflected his pleasure of the fact that the prodigal was home and all was well, and the next half-hour passed in easy conversation and the inevitable reading of the morning papers. At least on the two men's side. Paige was as tightly wound up as a coiled spring and would have given the world to be able to tell Declan exactly what she thought of him. Again.

He had no conscience, she thought furiously, no sense of moral fairness. He *knew* he was the last person she wanted to spend the day with and that was exactly why he had contrived the situation. It was all a game to him, an amusing diversion in his normally hectic life of big business in the world of finance. She had met plenty of men like him since starting work.

As soon as she could decently make her escape she
shot up to her room, leaving the two men at the table
reminiscing now on days gone by. 'I'll meet you down
here at ten,' Declan said lazily as she reached the
doorway, and she nodded carefully without turning
round, keeping her voice bright even as her eyes froze.
'Lovely, thank you.' Lovely? She ground her teeth
as she walked up the stairs. This was going to kill her,
she thought crossly as she reached her room and sank
weakly on the wide soft bed. What did he mean, he
was here until the weekend? Till Friday, or actually
staying the weekend? Please don't let him stay the
whole weekend, she prayed avidly as she stood up in
one jerky movement and walked over to the window,
staring down blindly into the beautifully tended
gardens below. She could, possibly, just keep up this
awful masquerade for another forty-eight hours, but
beyond that she would end up doing something crimi-
nal! He was so infuriatingly superior, so in control,
so utterly sure of himself that it made her blood boil.

Declan was waiting for her when she strolled, with
studied casualness, down the stairs at ten, and she
greeted him with a cool smile as she reached his side,
which disappeared like magic as he placed a light kiss
on the top of her head.

'Don't do that!' she spat quietly, flushing violently.

'Why not?' He peered down at her with mocking
innocence, his face alive with amusement as the smell
of him encompassed her in a delicious thrill she could
have done without. 'It's just a little brotherly kiss.'
The dark face dared her to disagree.

'You aren't my brother,' she said tightly. 'We aren't related even in the most distant sense and you know it.'

'No, we aren't, are we?' he drawled thoughtfully, his eyes dancing wickedly. 'But it will do for an excuse until I can think of something better.'

'I don't want anything to do with you, Declan, so let's get that straight from the start,' she said flatly as she stepped backwards, putting some space between them. 'I mean it.'

'You don't know what you're missing.' He eyed her slowly from head to foot. 'Do you?' She ignored the pointed question with regal disdain, walking with careful coolness towards the end of the hall. She wasn't going to allow any probing about her love-life, not from him!

She glanced at him from under her eyelashes as he opened the front door, allowing her to precede him with a little bow. 'Your carriage awaits, child.' Again that little gibe!

'That's your car?' She stared at the silver metalwork glowing in the sun before turning to look up into the dry, sardonic face. 'Your own car?'

'Yes.' The grey eyes were guarded now. 'Why?'

'Oh, it's just that Matthew fell in love with it yesterday.' She couldn't resist repeating the latter part of their conversation. 'He thought it would probably be driven by an old-age pensioner in his dotage,' she continued sweetly.

'Did he?' The grim mouth told her he was not amused and she felt an overt thrill at piercing the cool façade. 'Well, you'll be able to tell him he was wrong, won't you?' She gave a little giggle as they walked down the steps and he glanced at her warily. 'What now?' He was clearly not finding this conversation amusing and she revelled in finding this unexpected vulnerable spot and intended to make the most of it.

'Do you have more money than sense, Declan?'

He stared at her for a moment and then indicated the car wryly. 'Another part of your conversation with the reputable Matthew? What does he drive? No, let me guess. A nice safe BMW? Am I right?' His voice was scathing.

'How did you——?' She stopped abruptly. 'You saw his car yesterday when he left!' she accused flatly.

'So I did.' He smiled softly. 'And standing on these very steps.' A sudden heat in the dark face told her he was remembering what had transpired immediately afterwards and she blushed hotly as she continued walking down to the car that was waiting for them with regal indifference. It didn't do to bandy words with him, she thought wryly; he would always win.

As she slid into the car she had the strangest feeling she was sitting on a level with the road, and as Declan joined her in the driver's seat she was immediately aware of hard-muscled thighs close to hers, the length of his long legs and the sheer male bulk of him uncomfortably close. What was it with him? she thought painfully. She had never had her femininity exposed so rawly before, and it grated, badly.

'Paige?' He had leant back in his seat and closed his eyes, and it was like this that he addressed her.

'Do something for me, would you?' His voice was very smooth and very relaxed.

'What?' she asked warily.

'Relax. You look scared to death and it makes me feel you expect me to leap on you at any moment. Now, while the idea is not unappealing, at ten o'clock in the morning, after a hearty breakfast, and being positioned in a rather unsuitable car for such activities, *and* right outside our mutual parents' bedroom window, I think you can assume that in this instance, at least, you are pretty safe.' The tone of his voice hadn't altered at all.

'You're a pig,' she said weakly, and he laughed softly.

'You say such sweet things.' He opened his eyes and turned to face her, resting one arm on the wheel and sliding the other along the back of her seat. She steeled herself to show no reaction. After his former comments any response would be too humiliating to bear. 'You look remarkably like a delicious little honey-pot,' he said thoughtfully as his eyes stroked her face slowly. 'All tasty and soft and silky, but I have the notion that if I tried a spoonful it would be bitter. For me at any rate. Am I right?'

She shrugged tightly. 'You'll never know.'

'And Matthew?' Now the silver-grey gaze had sharpened into pure steel. 'Where does he fit in? Is he the current boyfriend?'

She shrugged again. 'What is this? Twenty questions?' She turned to undo her window but searched helplessly for a button or handle until he turned the ignition key, activating the engine into a low purr, and flicked a switch on the dashboard which lowered the window automatically. 'Thank you.' She deliberately turned away, her face scarlet.

'My pleasure.' He gave her one last long look and then fastened his seatbelt, easing the powerful car in a tight circle on the wide drive and then cruising past the avenue of trees on either side to the open gates which led on to the quiet country road, his movements calm, relaxed and unhurried.

She sat quite still, her head in a whirl and her hands clenched in her lap. She had the feeling he would control everything as effortlessly as he had that window, and suddenly the thought had the power to terrify her. She had been crazy to think of getting even with him; you didn't make a declaration of war on a vastly superior force unless you wanted to be utterly crushed in the process. She disliked him, she would *always* dislike him, but all she wanted to do now was to get through the next couple of days with as little contact between them as possible and then put him out of her mind. A deep, primitive sense of survival, an age-old instinct, was telling her that it was essential to her future peace of mind that she treat this man as untouchable. Let him in, even in the slightest way, and the agony and heartache she had suffered at his hands in the past would be nothing to what the future would hold. He was poison.

CHAPTER THREE

'WOULD you like to tell me where to go?' The quiet gravelly voice broke into Paige's churning thoughts abruptly and she drew a deep unsteady breath as she glanced at the rugged profile.

'What?'

'Would——?' Declan stopped abruptly. 'No, hang on, let me re-phrase that. The original was like putting a loaded gun into your hands with the trigger pointed in my direction.'

'I don't know what you're talking about,' she said tightly.

'What direction do you want me to take? Town or country?' He glanced at her swiftly as she sat silently by his side. 'There are crossroads up ahead. You'll have to make up your mind.'

'Crossroads?' She pulled her thoughts into order with some considerable effort. He would think she was mentally deficient if she carried on like this. 'Oh, I don't mind.'

He gave a deep sigh of exasperation. 'Paige, this little trip was your idea, remember? Shopping and a drive in the country? Now which comes first?'

The thought of walking as a couple round the country town's little cobbled centre was as un-thinkable as an intimate drive in the country in this souped-up time bomb, and as she hesitated they approached, and passed, the crossroads. 'Decision made,' he said calmly. 'A drive in the country, lunch at a little pub I know and then shopping later. OK?'

'Look, Declan——'

'Do you like home-made steak and kidney pudding?' he asked cheerfully as though she hadn't spoken. 'They do the best one I've ever tasted at the Horse and Penny, and the raspberry pie is out of this world.' He eyed her quizzically for a split-second. 'And do drag a smile up from somewhere when we arrive, please. The landlord happens to be a friend and he'll think I'm losing my touch if you walk in looking like that.'

'Huh!' The exclamation spoke volumes and he laughed softly at her outraged face.

'I know, I'm a pig,' he said with cool self-mockery.

It was a pleasant run through the quiet English countryside, the soft rolling green hills and wooded slopes pleasing to the eye, and in other circumstances she would have enjoyed the ride on such a beautiful summer's day. Today, however, she was painfully aware of every tiny movement Declan made, of his hard brown hands on the wheel and the way the lean, powerful body controlled the low, sleek car with the minimum of effort.

Thoughts she could well have done without came popping into her mind from nowhere and she was immensely thankful he didn't have the power to read her mind. She had never wondered what any other man would look like naked, but she found herself wondering it about him and it shocked her. The clean lemony smell of him tantalised her nostrils at odd moments when the warm breeze from the open windows caught the air-flow just right, and she wondered if her perfume was affecting him in the same way. Probably not, she thought wryly. He was made of stone. And she didn't like him anyway. She *definitely* didn't like him!

'Here we are.' The approach to the small village had been down a steep hill with a sharp left-hand bend at the bottom, but the narrow road and difficult access had made it a virtual no-go area for the heavy lorries that trundled through other once quiet and peaceful spots, and the village sat in gentle tranquillity, basking comfortably in the warm sunshine as they drew to a halt outside the unusual-looking pub.

'Jon is originally from Switzerland,' Declan explained as he noticed her glance of surprise at the distinctive cottage *'ornée'* style of the building in front of them. 'He married a local girl and they had only been here a year when the old pub burnt down. He rebuilt on the land and decided to go for an alpine look to remind him of home. Fits in well, though, doesn't it?' He looked down at her quietly.

'Yes, it does,' she agreed slowly. The steeply pitched roof, decorative barge boarding and tile-hung upper storey did adapt to the limestone scenery all around, and the little spire on top of the house and the magnificent garden rich with a gay riot of colour and the drone of bees were pure England.

'Sit down.' Declan indicated a table for two surrounded by a host of orange marigolds and nodded politely at the only other inhabitant sitting on an old wooden bench to one side of the arched door, a gnarled, bent old man whose lined face smiled benevolently at them both. 'I'll let Jon know we're here. Draught cider OK?' He was already walking away.

'Fine.' She perched uneasily on the edge of her chair as Declan disappeared into the interior of the pub. What was she doing here? How on earth had all this happened? She didn't want to be having lunch with her estranged stepbrother in a beautiful country garden in the middle of nowhere, and he probably didn't want to be having lunch with her! He had engineered the whole thing just to prove a point. Her eyes were green with irritation. What sort of woman would he usually lunch with? She caught the thought abruptly. Who cared?

'There.' Declan set a glass of cider down in front of her and frowned at her tight face. 'Smile, Paige, Jon is coming out in a minute.' The tone was wry and faintly mocking but it caught her on the raw.

'If you wanted to have lunch with someone who would hang on your every word and boost your already over-inflated ego, you shouldn't have asked me, should you?' she snapped crossly. 'I'm not putting on a show for your friend!'

The amused gleam in his eyes faded and his face straightened slowly. 'You really are a little shrew, aren't you?' he said softly. 'Who's made you like that, Paige, or is it natural? Your mother is a natural lady. What happened to you?'

'A natural lady?' Annoyingly, the criticism hurt. 'How can you say——?' She stopped abruptly. She had almost been going to say she had thought he considered her mother a mercenary gold-digger but she mustn't, couldn't give herself away. 'I'm glad you appreciate her,' she said instead, her eyes shooting sparks at his watchful face. 'Have you always held this high opinion of her?' Wriggle out of that one, she thought balefully, as his eyes held hers for a moment more and then turned away.

'Here's Jon,' he said unemotionally, and she glared at his broad back as his friend approached. Saved by the bell!

'I'm pleased to meet you, Paige.' The tall blond man in front of her spoke English with a heavy accent but his round face was warm and smiling and she liked him instantly. 'You are going to try my steak and kidney pudding, I understand?'

'Yes, please.' She smiled up at him and held out her hand. 'I'm pleased to meet you too, Jon, and I love your pub.'

'This is true?' He shook her hand vigorously and then turned to Declan with a ear-splitting smile. 'I like your Paige, Declan.'

'Good.' Declan had watched the proceedings with a small cynical smile playing at the corner of his mouth and a guarded expression in his eyes she couldn't quite fathom. 'But she isn't mine, Jon, not this one,' he finished enigmatically.

'No?' Jon glanced from one to the other and then smiled conspiratorially at Paige. 'This, I think, is a pity. He needs a good woman, Paige.'

'A bad one is more fun,' Declan drawled slowly. 'Just because you're an old married man, don't consign me to the same fate.' In spite of the lightness Paige felt he meant what he said.

'I have some news for you,' Jon said proudly. 'I am soon to be a father too. In November.'

In the ensuing congratulations and back-slapping Declan's remark was forgotten, but as they sat waiting in the perfumed air for the meal she remembered his dry, cynical voice, and darted a quick glance at his face from under her eyelashes, catching the full force of that silvery gaze as she looked his way. A little chill of awareness fluttered down her spine.

'Well?' He stretched his legs and took a long pull of cider. 'What was that look for?' he asked expressionlessly.

She was going to explain it away but then some perverse curiosity persuaded her to ask what was in her mind. 'That remark you made to Jon,' she said carefully. 'Were you joking?'

'What remark?' His face hardened but she didn't notice.

'About not wanting to get married.' She wished she had never started this now as her cheeks turned pink. So much for not delving into his mind!

He stared at her for a long moment, his harsh face implacable, and then he shrugged slowly, his eyes hooded and cool. 'I've got nothing against marriage for those who need it,' he said slowly. 'It's just not something I'd indulge in myself.'

'Why not?' In for a penny, in for a pound, she thought to herself wryly.

'I prefer to keep my options open and my life uncluttered,' he said shortly. 'I answer to myself and myself alone.'

'That sounds very cold-blooded.' She ran her finger round the top of the glass as she spoke. 'Don't you want children eventually, a settled home, slippers in front of the fire and all that? Not now necessarily, but perhaps in a few years when you're older?'

'No.' He clearly had no intention of elaborating and she felt slightly nonplussed.

'Oh.' She blinked quickly. 'Well, I do.'

'Most women do.' He eyed her unsmilingly. 'The "broody hen syndrome", but by the time you find out it's not enough it's too late.'

It was said with such coldness that she blinked again, totally out of her depth. There was an icy aloofness about him now that intrigued her even as she told herself to forget it. He meant nothing to her; what did it matter anyway?

'Here's the meal.' As Jon approached with a loaded tray Declan switched back to attentive companion at the blink of an eye, his face bland now and his voice smooth. 'My compliments to the chef, Jon,' he said smilingly. 'I presume Tricia still does all the cooking?'

Jon nodded smilingly. '*Bon appetit*.'

After Jon returned to the bar and they started their meal Paige found her mind straying back to their previous conversation. He had been so cold when he spoke of marriage. What could he possibly have against it? To her knowledge he had never even been engaged, let alone married. She glanced at him now as he sat eating the delicious food with every appearance of enjoyment. He was such a complex man, able to mask his emotions at will and totally in charge of himself and the world around him. She would ask her mother about him when they returned to the house. She nodded mentally. It wouldn't do any harm to find out a bit about him; he wouldn't know. And it might give her an edge.

He stood up suddenly and as she glanced at him he leant over the table, loosening her hair from its clip and slipping the ribbon in his pocket. 'What...?' She raised a hand to her hair as it fell in silky waves about her face.

'I like it loose,' he said softly, 'and if I had asked you to wear it like that you would have refused.' His audacity left her momentarily gasping for words and he smiled humorously at her angry face, the first real smile she had seen. It transformed the harsh, somewhat rough features in a way she could not have imagined, bringing a vulnerability to the hard male face that made her breath catch in her throat. What had he looked like as a little boy? Even as the thought surfaced, a little segment of her mind screamed caution and she lowered her eyes instantly, her voice curt.

'You really are the most impossible man I've ever met.'

'Do you know, you aren't the first to say that?' he said mildly. 'I really can't understand why.'

The raspberry pie was as delicious as he had said but eating was difficult. Her mind was filled with so many conflicting emotions it was making her head ache, and the physical sensations Declan induced were more worrying than pleasant. It was almost as though he had transported her back in time to being a shy, uncertain sixteen-year-old, and she felt angry with him and herself for feeling that way. Her brain was telling her he was beneath contempt, a cruel, unfeeling tyrant of a man who had cut his father off for years because he had committed the terrible sin of marrying the woman he loved; but then, when she looked at him, that almost tangible 'something' took her breath away. She was weak, pathetically weak, she told herself sharply, and if she let him sense it, even for a moment, she knew he would capitalise on such a perfect opportunity with all the determination that cold, analytical mind was capable of.

'You don't smile much, do you?' She had been unaware that he was watching her and now she raised her head sharply, the frown that had creased her forehead at her dismal thoughts deepening.

'It depends who I'm with,' she said coldly.

'Ow!' He shook his fingertips as though they had been burnt. 'You've certainly got a tongue on you, Paige Green. And a temper to match that glorious hair. Who does it come from, by the way? Your father?'

'Yes.' She glanced at his own black hair. 'And your colouring? Your mother?'

'Uh-huh.' Suddenly the drawbridge had been raised again and that remote expression was turning the silver-grey eyes into ice.

'I don't think I've ever seen her picture,' she said as she finished the last mouthful of pie. 'Do you have one?'

'Yes.' He stood up abruptly and she saw his face was dark and closed. 'Coffee?'

The snub was piercingly fierce, and as hot colour flooded her face she stared up at him as anger warred with her intention to stay cool and calm. Anger won. 'Do you have to be so rude?' she asked tightly. 'You did mention my father first after all. I really don't see——'

'That is the trouble with your sex,' he said coldly as the ice in his eyes chilled her blood. 'You never do see anything at all unless it's right in front of your nose.'

'Oh, really?' She was too angry now to consider her words. 'And I suppose you're perfect, are you? Well, not from where I'm standing, Mr Wonderful Stone. In fact I think you are the biggest creep I've met for a long time!'

'I think I was already aware of that,' he said grimly. 'Now, do you want coffee?' He was so cold, so austere, so uncaring. She stared up at him in outrage. She had never met such a hateful man before in her life! He made some of the sharks she dealt with in her day-to-day life in the fashion world seem like sweet little pussycats.

'Black, please.' She held his gaze with acid determination until after a long, tense moment he turned and walked into the dark interior of the pub without a backward glance.

'I apologise.'

'What?' She had shut her eyes after he had gone, and now they snapped open at the quiet voice at her elbow.

'You said nothing wrong; the fault was mine.' He had returned as silently as a panther to crouch at her

side, his face on a level with her own. 'You were
making conversation and I was very rude.' He kissed
the top of her nose lightly as he stood up and for a
moment her heart stood still. 'There are some things
I find it difficult to talk about and my mother is one
of them.' The dark face was very wary and curiously
vulnerable.

She barely heard his last words. He had been so
close that she could have run her hands through the
dark body hair visible through the open shirt, and to
her horror she had wanted to—she had wanted to!
Her stomach curled in protest but she couldn't deny
the almost overwhelming response her body had made
to his. It shocked her, it humiliated her, but it was
there.

And the apology, the unexpectedness of it, coupled
with the uncompromising honesty, had temporarily
thrown her. She stared at him dumbly. She couldn't
afford any chinks in her armour where he was concerned, but he was making it difficult—very difficult.

'Well?' He looked down at her unsmilingly, his face
watchful. 'Am I forgiven for such uncalled-for
boorishness?'

'Of course.' She smiled carefully as her heart
pounded almost painfully. She mustn't let him guess
how he unnerved her. 'Let's just forget it, shall we?'
Nice and cool, Paige.

'Still fancy that coffee?' He smiled at her nod and
disappeared back into the pub, leaving her in a
whirling confused daze.

The birds still sang in a startling blue sky, the scent
of summer flowers surrounded her in warm perfume,

everything was right in her world, and yet everything was wrong! The sooner she got back to her carefully constructed life the better, she thought desperately. Her interesting job, the occasional dates with Matthew, her delightful little flat... They were safe and normal and ordinary, and they had never seemed so dear.

Jon carried the coffee out a few minutes later, and as she glanced enquiringly behind him the blond man smiled apologetically. 'He is just talking to Tricia for a moment,' he said quickly. 'She is finishing a special sauce and then she will come to make your acquaintance.'

'Oh... right.' Paige smiled back into the handsome face. 'This is a lovely part of the world, Jon.'

'I agree.' There was immense satisfaction in the quiet words. 'I shall like to bring up my children here. We owe Declan more than words can say.'

'Declan?' She stared at him in surprise. 'I'm sorry, I don't quite follow.'

'But I understand you are Brenda's daughter? That you are family? I thought he would have told you...' The heavily accented voice died away in embarrassment. 'I should not have spoken,' he finished quickly; 'please to forget it.'

'Please, Jon.' Paige glanced up imploringly. 'To be honest I would like to understand Declan better; we haven't had any contact in the last few years. If you can tell me anything that might help...'

'Well...' He sat down by her side and began to place the contents of the tray on the table. 'I do not know if this will help really, but as far as I know it is no secret. However, as he has not told you, I would prefer that you do not——'

'I won't say a word,' she promised quickly, feeling a little dart of excitement start her heart pounding.

'We had not been here long when the premises were destroyed,' Jon said hesitantly, and Paige nodded in remembrance.

'Yes, Declan told me; it must have been awful for you.'

'It was very distressing, yes,' Jon said slowly, 'but the main problem was that we found we were grossly under-insured. The previous owners had not increased their insurance for years and we just took their figure as our sum. Very foolish, very foolish indeed, but there was a lot happening at that time. We had put all our savings into buying this place and Tricia's parents had come in—how do you put it—in a half?'

'Halves, yes,' Paige nodded understandingly.

'And suddenly we found that even with a mortgage and cutting costs it could not be done, and certainly not with the ideas I had for rebuilding. I had known Declan for years and somehow through a mutual friend he got to hear about things and the next thing we know he is down here with his cheque-book.' Jon shook his head at the memory. 'He wanted to *give* us the money but we could not accept that, Paige, it would not be right.'

'No, I suppose not,' Paige said faintly as her mind tried to take in the fact that they were really talking about Declan, the whiz-kid financier, hard as nails, ruthless . . .

'So he insisted on an interest-free loan, to be repaid at some time in the future but without legal ties, a "gentleman's" agreement.' Jon's voice held the note of incredulity that it must have had when Declan had first made the proposal.

'And so...' he waved his arms expansively. '... the dream became a reality, but with no crippling mortgage, no worry, no sleepless nights. He is a good friend,' he finished soberly. 'The best.'

She was saved from trying to make a reply by the reappearance of Declan accompanied by a beaming Tricia, for which she was heartily thankful as all lucid thought seemed paralysed. As the four of them sat and made small talk she found her mind was functioning somewhere quite different. The world that Declan inhabited was dog-eat-dog, she knew that from various comments Gerald had made in the past; a world where the ruthless survived and the weak perished. And yet... She glanced at him out of the corner of her eye as he laughed softly at something Tricia had said. How many men were there under that skin?

By the time she was settled back in the car as they prepared to leave, her thoughts were in turmoil. She needed to pull herself together, she told herself desperately. The revelation by Jon, the memory of how good it felt to be in his arms, the warmth in his face as he had talked to his two friends... It hadn't done her any good at all.

'I hear you've done very well for yourself.' He slid into his seat by her side and turned to her, his hands on the wheel. 'Brenda is very proud of you.' The silver eyes caught her gaze.

'Is she?' Paige smiled carefully as her heart thudded. 'I've had to work hard but it's worth it. I love my job.'

He nodded slowly. 'Design, isn't it?' As the engine purred into life he backed slowly out of the small car park and into the narrow country road. 'I was surprised you'd gone into that area when I heard. I'd had you down for a nurse, or nanny, or——'

The casual surprise in his voice brought the harsh words he had spoken so long ago flashing into her mind as though it were yesterday, wiping away the softer image as though by magic.

How could she have forgotten, even for a minute, what havoc his scathing judgement had wrought in her life, and his opinion of her mother? How could she have forgotten? But she had, briefly, until he had reminded her again.

'Drudge?' she said crisply, her eyes shadowed and deep. That would suit the picture he had so cruelly drawn of her perfectly after all, and she was shocked and angry at how much it still hurt. A plain little schoolgirl with spots and a brace didn't venture into the high-profile world of design.

'Drudge?' The note of amazement in his voice sounded genuine. 'Of course not. It was just that I pictured you with people somehow, helping, looking after them, I don't know.'

He shrugged slowly as he negotiated the sharp bend and urged the powerful car up the sloping hill. 'Still,

I hadn't seen you for years, had I? People change a lot in their teens.'

'This one certainly did.' In her effort to keep all hurt and pain out of her voice it sounded caustic, even harsh, and as the tone registered on his ears he shook his dark head slowly as he kept his eyes on the narrow winding road ahead.

There was an expression on the hard face that she couldn't quite read, of disappointment maybe, of pain, but perhaps she was imagining things again. It wasn't hard to do that around him.

He didn't speak for almost a full minute and by then his face was its usual sardonic mask, cool and dark.

'I remember a gentle, shy girl who wouldn't say boo to a goose. I guess you could say you'd changed.' His facial expression and dry voice made it quite clear he considered it a change for the worse, and she clenched her hands in protest.

'Gentle, shy girls get trampled on,' she said bitterly, a stab of pain that she couldn't quite hide spiking her words.

'Someone hurt you?' He turned sharply to glance at her and then swore softly as his eyes returned to the road and he had to swerve away from the kerb. 'Do you want to talk about it?'

'It was a long time ago,' she said tightly, leaning forward and slipping a cassette into the appropriate slot to signify the conversation was at an end. There were some things *she* didn't like to talk about as well! Someone hurt her? How right he was!

He took the hint and there was a tense, biting silence between them as they drove through the countryside, passing another village where the church was standing in a churchyard so steep that it would seem some of the inhabitants would have had to be buried vertically.

'Are you interested in history?' Declan asked when the silence was deafening, his voice easy and expressionless.

'History?' She glanced at the austere profile and nodded slowly. 'I suppose so, sometimes.'

'It's just that the next village is particularly steeped in it if you're tempted. There's a fine old manor house that's open to the public and a working smithy in the main street. Does that appeal more than shopping? It's up to you.'

'Yes, OK.' She glanced at her watch. 'That would be better, actually; I don't want to be late back. Matthew is ringing at six.' She tried to match her tone to his.

'Is he?' There was deep sarcasm in the gravelly voice. 'Well, of course we mustn't keep Matthew waiting, heaven forbid.'

She had been going to explain that Matthew was phoning her to tell her the results of her latest designs—they had been going before the board meeting that afternoon with a decision on whether production would go ahead—but in view of his unjustified derision she said nothing. Let him think what he liked! This was one woman who wouldn't fawn over him!

As Declan drew into the attractive grounds leading to the handsome old house she looked about her with interest. The regulation formality of the neat flowerbeds and smooth lawns told her it was well cared for, and to her delight she spied a maze to the far side of the house. In other circumstances, with a different companion, that might have been fun, she thought wistfully, but the thought of wandering in there with Declan sent a shiver trickling down her spine that was nothing to do with fear but still signified danger.

The house was beautiful and she especially liked the Turkish room, inspired by the private apartments of seventeenth-century sultans in Istanbul. The décor was magnificent and the furnishings lavish, and the billowing silk that lined the walls and flowed over to the low beds and scattered cushions was rich and seductively sensual. 'This has given me an idea for my bedroom,' Declan drawled blandly in her ear as she stood admiring the room. 'After seeing the look on your face I think it would be a winner with the ladies, yes?' He smiled slowly, and the insidious pull at her heartstrings jerked uncomfortably.

She shrugged offhandedly as her flesh tickled. 'You need help in the bedroom?' she asked mockingly.

He laughed softly. 'Not exactly, but atmosphere helps. Don't you find all this silk and richness appealing?'

'I don't think——' She turned to make a light remark but found herself staring into his face instead, and there was something dark and warm in the narrowed eyes that caused the words to die on her lips, the wry twist to his mouth beckoning.

'Paige...' He cupped her face in his hands, bending down to take her lips as he did so, and as she felt their touch her insides melted. Like before, it was as though a flame ignited that would consume them both, and as the kiss deepened she felt she was drowning, being drawn into his body until she was liquid. His mouth moved to her throat where an agitated pulse beat. The sound of other visitors approaching the room broke the spell, and as Declan moved away his face was rueful. 'Come on, let's visit the smithy,' he said quietly, taking her hand in a light hold.

She wandered round the old rough-hewn smithy in a daze, hardly listening as the skilled blacksmith explained that his main living came from repairs to farm machinery these days and quite unable to concentrate as they stood and watched him hammering new harrow rings out of a mild steel rod. Declan was going to kiss her again, she just knew it, and she had to stop it this time. It was madness, this feeling that would keep persisting. This was Declan, for goodness' sake, cold, hard Declan, who would use her for a light affair, a momentary diversion, before returning to his world. Where was her pride? Where was all the anger and the cold desire for revenge she had saved up through the years? He wasn't even pretending he particularly liked her, for goodness' sake, beyond a physical attraction.

As they walked back down the quiet leafy lane from the smithy towards the car still parked in the grounds of the old house, he took her hand in his. His touch was casual, but she was vitally aware of his tall, broad figure next to her, of the strong, hard arms covered in dark curling hair and his long legs under the light trousers. She felt gauche and young and stupid, like a schoolgirl on a date with an experienced man of the world, and the feeling intensified as she realised they had left the main path and he had drawn her into a little shady dell hidden from the road and shaded by tall trees and dense grass.

'Declan, we need to get back.' She tried to make her voice firm.

'It's too hot to get back in the car for a while,' he said easily. 'We've plenty of time. Have a seat.' He indicated the carpet of thick springy grass inter-weaved with tiny starry flowers and clover and flung himself down, stretching out on his back with his hands beneath his head, his eyes shut.

She stood for a moment, uncertain of what to do next, and then carefully seated herself a few feet away from his still form, her heart thudding in her chest and her hands damp with apprehension. Was this a seduction scene or just what it seemed on a surface level? She didn't know, and she bit her lower lip anxiously. She didn't know him, she certainly didn't know herself; she suddenly felt she didn't know anything any more!

It was amazingly quiet in the secluded little copse, the intermittent drone of lazy insects and twittering of birds overhead the only sound apart from the odd car going past on the winding lane once or twice. As the minutes ticked by she began to relax a little. Declan hadn't spoken since he had lain down; in fact he seemed to have dozed off. She peered at him now, carefully at first and then more searchingly as his heavy breathing reassured her that he was asleep.

The position of his hands behind his head had stretched the silk of his shirt tight over his chest and she could see the muscles rippling just below the surface of his skin. His arms were strong and sinewy, his legs powerful. He must be very fit, she thought idly as her eyes ran over his lean frame from head to foot. Very fit, very athletic, very vigorous... He was an uncomfortable man to be around, she decided as her eyes hesitated on his slim thighs. Too potently male to ignore, too lusty...

The thought brought her head snapping down as though she had voiced it out loud. What was the matter with her? she thought distractedly. She had always thought it was the male sex that had unruly thoughts of this nature; she certainly hadn't been bothered by them before, but now they were filling her mind with disturbing images that she was at a loss to banish.

She felt hot and flustered as she raised her head again, and this time it was to look straight into his eyes as he raised himself slightly, propping his head on his hand, his elbow resting on the grass. 'I thought if I relaxed you'd do the same, but you're as nervy as a kitten,' he said slowly. 'Are you always like this? No wonder you're so slim.'

'Not always, no,' she said tightly as she flicked an imaginary piece of grass off her trousers.

In one lithe movement he rolled over to her side, resuming the position again as he looked up into her face. 'Is it me, then?' he asked softly. 'I worry you in some way?' She took a hidden breath. It *was* a seduction scene. She should have known!

'Look, Declan, I think we ought to be getting back,' she said faintly, preparing to rise until his hand restrained her. 'And don't touch me,' she snapped quickly, all caution and tact deserting her in the face of his nearness.

'Why not?' he asked mildly. 'I don't bite—at least, if I do it's only in the very nicest way.' He smiled wickedly but she was in no mood for such talk. It awakened feelings in her lower limbs that she could well do without.

'Are we going?' She looked down pointedly at his hand on her arm but he ignored the action with regal indifference.

'Relax, Paige, take a few minutes out of life to relax.' His voice was deep and husky, and as she looked into the silver gaze she felt mesmerised and helplessly excited, unable to resist as the hand on her arm drew her inexorably down beside him until she was stretched out on the warm grass, almost quivering with anticipation. As his lips gently touched her creamy throat in soft burning kisses she felt herself begin to tremble, and then his mouth was moving all over her face, her ears, her neck, until she was almost begging him to take her mouth. The smell, the feel of him filled her whole mind.

'You are the most tantalisingly delicious...' His voice was lost as he claimed her mouth at last, moving over her so she could feel every inch of his body, his arousal obvious. She put her arms round his neck, drawing him even closer against her softness, and heard him groan deep in his throat as his body stirred against hers. His kisses were thrilling and she was barely conscious of his hands moving across her body, her whole being tuned into one trembling whole of sensation. He broke away once to bury his face in the red silk of her hair but she searched for his mouth until his lips met hers, unaware of what she was doing, lost in this, her first taste of sensual pleasure as his fingers brushed her flesh caressingly.

'Hell, I must stop this, Paige.' As his muttered groan registered on her mind she realised he was pulling away and the next instant he had sat up, running a hand through the dark shock of hair and then springing to his feet. 'That's enough. I'm sorry, Paige, I shouldn't have done that.' As he stood looking down at her she saw with a little shock of horror that there was a look of disgust on his face, and she was too inexperienced to recognise that it was directed at himself rather than her. Her blood ran cold.

'Declan?' She hastily smoothed her clothes into order as she too sat up, her cheeks burning with humiliation as she tried to focus her thoughts. It should have been she who had stopped the madness, not he. He must think she was so easy.

Her thoughts were written on her face for him to read and he knelt swiftly at her side, his face tightening as she flinched away. 'It was my fault; I should have known better. I've been playing with fire all day, but you're so damn sweet...' He stood up again, thrusting his hands into his pockets as he turned his back on her. 'Have you slept with anyone before, Paige? Matthew? Anyone?' His voice was suddenly hard.

The question should have annoyed her but she was unable to feel anything through the numbness that was taking hold. Now their lovemaking had stopped she realised just how near Declan had come to taking her, and the thought was burningly painful.

'No,' she said flatly as she stared vacantly ahead.

'I thought not.' The broad back was stiff as he still didn't turn his head. How could she have succumbed so utterly, so fast? 'I couldn't believe it last night when I felt your inexperience. Looking the way you do, in my world you'd be on your tenth affair by now.' Dark cynicism threaded his deep voice.

'Would I?' Her voice was mechanical, wooden, but that was how she felt. What was he talking about—affairs, his world? The world was here, now, with this coldness that seemed to have filled every crevice of her mind even as her flesh burnt hotly.

'I suppose I wanted to see if it was real,' he said almost to himself. 'You're so lovely, Paige, so fresh, so unspoilt.'

His words hammered on her mind. He had wanted to see if it was real! All this had been a game with him, a cold-blooded exercise to feed his male ego, to see if he could get her to succumb?

'I want to go home.' She stood up slowly and faced him, her face white with a mixture of self-contempt at her own weakness and bitter rage at his cruelty. 'Now.'

'Don't look like that.' He reached across to touch her face but she recoiled from him so sharply she almost fell.

'Stay away from me, Declan.' Her eyes blazed into his, and there was such hate and anger in their depths that he couldn't fail to see it. 'You've had your fun, you've proved that you could have taken me if you'd wanted to. Isn't that enough?'

'Paige, it's not like that—listen——'

'I'll *walk* home if you won't drive me!' Her voice was rising on the edge of hysteria and he stepped back with his palms held uppermost, his voice calming and his eyes withdrawn.

'OK, OK. We'll go now.'

She sat huddled in the car all the way home, her face turned to the window and her hair providing a veil against his eyes. She had always despised the type of girl who fell into bed with a man on the first date but now she realised that some of them, at least, might have been lost before a more experienced and clever mind. She should never have gone into that secluded copse with him, never sat down, never—— She jerked her thoughts savagely into order. Hindsight was all very well, but he—*he* had known what he was doing.

And hadn't she? She almost groaned at the small accusing voice in her mind. Not really, no, she hadn't. She would never have believed that passion and desire were such strong, overwhelmingly fierce weapons. But she knew now. She took a deep breath as Gerald's house came into view. And she would never make the same mistake again. She had been hurt twice by this man. She would make sure there was never a third time.

CHAPTER FOUR

As PAIGE opened the front door of her flat she realised she couldn't feel her feet any more and the fingers holding the key were numb with cold. December the twenty-third. She grimaced to herself apprehensively as she flung her portfolio on to an easy-chair along with a small suitcase containing a number of sketches and samples of material. She hadn't been able to think of Christmas this year without her heart doing crazy somersaults at the thought that Declan might, just might, have the nerve to appear despite the way they had parted company after that day in the summer.

Since August, when her adventurous designs had been snapped up first by Matthew's father and his partner, and then by their wealthy clientele who had embraced Paige's new ideas with rapturous enthusiasm, she had been working non-stop.

It had proved a blessing after the disastrous weekend following Gerald's birthday. She hadn't had a minute to think or brood with self-destructive post-mortems, working as she was seven days a week with hastily snatched meals and little sleep, but she had to admit that the constant hard grind was catching up with her. She nodded to herself as she switched on the faithful coffee-maker, and kicked off her shoes thankfully. She'd have to slow down; Matthew had been saying it for weeks. Life was hectic and exciting and full but somehow, in spite of all the good things that were happening to her, there was something missing, and she didn't know what it was.

She smiled ruefully as she fixed a rather sad-looking sandwich with the last of the cheese and tomatoes from her empty fridge. 'The human animal is never satisfied.' It was a saying of Gerald's, and like several other of his little axioms it held more than a grain of truth.

The churning feeling in her stomach was very much in evidence as she drove down to Hertfordshire the next day. It was bitterly cold but dry and sunny, and normally she would have loved the pretty winding route to Gerald's house, relaxing and taking note of the countryside clothed in its stark winter beauty against a white-gold sky. But... She shrugged the 'but' away, annoyed with herself at the way her heart pounded as Declan's dark face flashed into her mind. He had shown her very clearly what he thought of her in the summer, using her almost as an experiment and being able to stop things without showing a shred of feeling, whereas she—— Her thoughts stopped abruptly. It had meant *nothing* to her too! *Nothing*. She nodded her head sharply.

She drew into Gerald's immaculate drive just as the sky was turning a dark vivid red streaked with soft shades of grey, and immediately saw the sight she had been dreading. Declan's sleek car eyed her broodingly, the massive low headlights staring at her with disdain and contempt and the exquisite silver paintwork glowing pink in the reflection of the dying day.

He *was* here, then! Her nerves screamed in protest and she forced herself to draw to a smooth halt and get out of the car slowly, the tingling flutter of excitement that fluttered down her spine causing her mouth to tighten in self-contempt. She had forced herself not to think of him for months, almost convinced herself he wouldn't have the nerve to instigate a 'family' Christmas after his treatment of her in the summer. But she should have known! Her hazel eyes hardened into green glass. That over-inflated ego didn't have words like 'consideration' and 'sensitivity' in its vocabulary. But how could she face him again?

'You look peaky, Miss Paige.' Millicent's greeting as she opened the door to Paige's light knock didn't add to her confidence one iota and she hastily pinched some colour into her pale cheeks before the door to the drawing-room opened.

'Paige, darling!' Her mother descended in a rush of softness and warmth and for a moment she had the crazy impulse to hide behind the maternal skirts like a child facing a severe headmaster. 'How are you? We hardly get to hear from you these days. You're working far too hard.'

Paige took a deep breath and emerged from her mother's hug with a bright smile and a little nod. 'You're probably right, but I'm here for five days now so let's make the most of it. How are you and Gerald?'

'Fine, darling, fine.' Her mother was drawing her to the open door, and as she stepped into the room

her head went up a notch and the smile became brittle.
Declan was standing at the far end of the room, one
arm resting on the beautifully carved wooden man-
telpiece below which a roaring log fire crackled and
spat, his dark presence dominating the brightness and
colour of the Christmas decorations and gaily
festooned tree.

'Hello, Paige.' The cool smile that accompanied his
greeting did nothing to warm the narrow-eyed stare
that held her transfixed, and as he moved away from
the fireplace and walked towards her she had to nerve
herself to stand still. As he reached her side she held
out her hand but he drew her carefully against him
for a brief moment, kissing her cheek lightly before
standing back a pace and looking down at her, his
face a controlled, distant mask. 'You've lost weight.'

She stared up at him in surprise as hot anger placed
two spots of burning colour in her pale cheeks. She
couldn't have said at that precise moment which annoyed her more; his casual, offhand embrace which
shouted his lack of interest in her, or the criticism of
her slender shape. She *had* lost weight, she knew that,
but there was no need for him to point it out so coldly.

'I've been working hard,' she said tightly as her
eyes flashed green fire. 'Deadlines to meet.'

'Too hard.' He frowned slightly. 'You'll make
yourself ill.' All this empty concern for her mother's
benefit? she thought wryly.

'I'm a big girl now.' With a cool smile she walked
over to the fire, holding out her hands to the leaping
flames and keeping her back to the room. 'Where's
Gerald?' When she had got her expression the way

she wanted it she turned round again, looking directly at her mother now. She *wouldn't* play his little games.

'Delivering a box of goodies to little Mrs Creedy in the village,' her mother said quietly as she indicated the cocktail cabinet with a wave of her hand. 'What would you like to drink, darling? Dinner will be ready in about an hour.'

'White wine, please.' She forced the bright smile into life again.

'I'll see to it.' As Declan moved forward and poured her a drink she wanted to scream at her mother to put him in his place. How dared he act as though he was part and parcel of their lives? But then, the sobering thought flashed into her consciousness with bruising honesty, he was, wasn't he? In fact he had more right to be in this, his father's house, than she did. The thought was painful and she sat down suddenly, accepting the glass with a stiff little nod without looking directly at Declan, although her blood was pounding in her veins at his nearness.

Once Gerald returned the evening passed without too many awkward moments, but she declined her stepfather's suggestion of midnight Mass in the village with a tired little shake of her head as they ate dinner. 'I'll get to bed if you don't mind,' she said quietly, keeping her eyes trained away from the dark, sardonic face opposite. She hadn't glanced at Declan once during the meal but had been aware of that silver gaze fixed on her face for most of it, and it was sending goose-pimples down her spine in the most uncomfortable way. 'Life has been hectic lately and I could do with catching up on some sleep.'

'Fine, darling, whatever you want,' her mother said quickly, and as Paige glanced up to smile her thanks she caught the worried glance that passed between Brenda and Gerald with a stab of guilt. This was going to be a wonderful Christmas, just wonderful, she thought bitterly, and it was all *his* fault! The object of her anger sat in easy silence, exchanging the odd word with his father now and again but otherwise quietly enigmatic and seemingly totally relaxed. She looked at him now as she drained the last of her coffee and it was as though he had been waiting for her glance, his silver eyes glittering and cold as they met hers, his face set and forbidding. His eyes held hers tightly.

'You're leaving us so soon?' he asked smoothly. 'Your mother has been on tenterhooks all day waiting for you to arrive.'

'It's all right, Declan,' Brenda said quickly before Paige could speak. 'We've masses of time to catch up on the news and I'd rather Paige get some sleep for now. But it's sweet of you to be concerned.' She touched his arm in a light little gesture and Paige was amazed to see Declan smile back at her mother, the harsh face warm for an instant.

Sweet! She almost ground her teeth in her rage. He was about as sweet as a boa constrictor, and just as cunning. She lowered her eyes quickly in case her thoughts were visible. He had obviously ingratiated himself into her mother's favour in the last few months, although she sensed there was still some tension between the two men—some deep-rooted tension. The thought surprised her, coming as it did at such an inopportune moment, but once it was given birth she realised she was right. There was a coolness, certainly on Declan's part, that even her mother's natural warmth had been unable to dispel. And yet he genuinely seemed to like her mother, so it couldn't be the old problem rearing its head again. Oh, who cared anyway?

She thought for an awful moment that she had spoken out loud, but as she raised her head she was relieved to see the others sipping their coffee in companionable silence. She needed a hot bath and a long sleep, and then the battle with Declan would be more equal.

'Goodnight, then.' As she stood up she put an arm round her mother's narrow shoulders and gave her a swift hug. 'See you in the morning.' She smiled her farewell at Gerald.

'Goodnight.' Declan's voice was bland as he forced her to acknowledge his presence, and her hackles rose at his insistence. 'Sleep well.' Was she the only one who could hear the dry mockery?

'I will.' She smiled coolly as she flicked her heavy fringe out of her eyes with a defiant little gesture of her head. 'There's nothing to disturb me here.' It was a challenge only Declan understood, and she saw her refusal to be intimidated by his propinquity register in the narrowing of the light grey eyes as a small smile touched the hard mouth.

'That's my girl.' It was said quietly and expressionlessly, but as the lazy gaze wandered over her flushed face she could have hit him. His girl? Over her dead body!

She was still smouldering an hour later as she lay in bed, wide awake and furiously irritated. Declan was dominating her thoughts to the point where she could have screamed with annoyance at herself. He was clearly going to be thoroughly obnoxious this holiday, getting under her skin as only he knew how and enjoying every moment of it! How she loathed him! She pictured the dark, austere face and hard, lean body and that strange little thrill that always accompanied such weakness shivered down her spine. 'I *do* loathe him!' She sat up in bed with an angry jerk as she said the words out loud and then groaned softly. Talking to herself again! She only did it round him. He'd send her mad if she weren't careful. And she needed some rest.

It was nearly two in the morning when she heard the others coming to bed and she had given up all thoughts of sleep by this time and was sitting reading a book in which she had no interest. She heard a whispered conversation outside her room and then the door of the adjoining room open and close. He wasn't in the room next to hers, was he? She found herself listening intently and then the sound of someone moving about confirmed her fears. He was! How could her mother put him in there? She realised the stupidity of the thought as soon as it had surfaced. It was Declan's old room, just as this was hers; of course that was where he would sleep.

She found her ears straining to catch his movements. The creak of the cane chair as he sat to take off his shoes, then silence for a few moments, followed by the splash of the shower in the *en suite* for a few minutes. Then silence again until the lack of noise told her he was in bed. She remembered that his bed was against the wall of her room; the two headboards would be touching if it weren't for the wall dividing them. The hot feeling that began in her feet worked upwards until she felt the tingle in every limb. Would he wear pyjamas or——? She bit her lip until it hurt. Stop it, for goodness' sake, Paige, she thought angrily. No doubt he was tucked up and fast asleep by now, totally oblivious to her presence, whereas she . . . She bit her lip again until she tasted blood. She was going loopy!

Christmas morning brought an exchange of presents that was embarrassing in itself. Paige had sailed down to breakfast after a troubled night of tossing and turning, resolutely ignoring the headache that was lodged over her eyes and determined to act the perfect daughter. All went reasonably well until the unwrapping of the presents under the tree, although her first sight of Declan, cool and wickedly attractive in dark jeans and black silk shirt, was a nasty moment. It was as he handed her the tiny gold package enveloped in a gold bow that she felt a moment's panic. 'You haven't bought me a present, have you?' she asked, her eyes wide with horror.

'Just a little something,' he said smoothly as hot colour flared under her cheekbones. 'A trinket, no more.' The 'trinket' turned out to be a pair of beautiful antique ruby earrings that must have cost him a small fortune, and as Paige glanced at them lying in the velvet-lined box she felt mortified. Why hadn't she thought to get him something—anything? It just hadn't crossed her mind. She had been so rigidly determined not to think of him that she had done too good a job! And now she felt awful.

'I haven't got you anything.' She glanced up into his dark face and surprised an expression of probing intentness and... And something she didn't want to investigate further. 'I'm sorry, I've been so busy and I wasn't sure you'd be here.'

'No problem.' He smiled easily and the look was gone. 'What can you buy for the man that has everything?' It was said lightly, but she was shocked at how much it hurt. But it was true! He didn't need this home, his father, her mother or her. *Certainly* not her. She glanced at him again as he stood talking to Gerald. Women would go down like nine-pins before that magnetic charm, and she had had a taste of how he made love. No, he certainly didn't need any of them. He was self-sufficient, satisfied with his life, master of his own destiny and yet, sometimes, when he let his guard slip for a brief instant, there was a kind of vulnerability to the hard mouth, a yearning... She caught herself in amazement. Vulnerable— *Declan*? She really was beginning to crack up! She had never met such a cruel, hard——

'Would you like a walk to the village before dinner?' Declan asked her suddenly as she was bundling discarded wrapping paper into a large plastic bag. 'We could have a drink in the pub and——'

'No!' She had spoken too abruptly and tried to back-track with a smile. 'No, thanks. I'll help Mum with the dinner.'

'No need,' Brenda said brightly. 'You go for a walk with Declan; it'll do you good. Blow the cobwebs away and——'

'I'll stay and help you,' she repeated firmly. Gerald and her mother did not understand, but she couldn't, she just couldn't be alone with Declan. Not at this moment in time.

'No, really, darling,' her mother continued tactlessly. 'There's——'

'Leave it, Brenda.' Gerald's quiet voice cut across his wife's cheerful ramblings with a thread of understanding in its depths. 'Paige is right. Let her have a quiet morning with you.' As she met Gerald's carefully blank gaze she was aware of Declan stiffening at her side and then, after a taut moment, smiling casually, but his eyes were as hard as steel.

'Sure, it was just an idea,' he said easily. 'Perhaps you'd like a drink, Father and we'll leave the women to it?'

'Yes, I would like that,' Gerald said at once, and within minutes the two men had left and Paige felt the air leave her body in a slow rush. But that sort of incident would happen again, he would make sure of it, and she couldn't avoid him forever. She felt her cheeks burn. And her headache was worse.

The lunch was delicious but she ate very little of it. There was a large lump lodged in her throat and her stomach felt as though she had just got off a roller-coaster. It was the worst Christmas she had ever had, she reflected miserably, and it should have been the best. Her career was taking off with a vengeance, her name was being bandied about in quite exalted circles,

and her mother and Gerald were the happiest she had
seen them, thanks to the healing of the rift with
Declan. But therein lay the root of all her problems.
She caught his eye over the festive table and he raised
a glass to her slowly, his expression wry. 'Merry
Christmas, Paige.'

'Thank you.' She eyed him sourly. 'The same to
you.'

'Many thanks.' She could see that he was struggling
to check his amusement, and then, as he continued
staring at her, his expression changed. The silver eyes
were suddenly softer, warmer, with a small flame
flickering in their depths that drew her inwards towards him until his whole face seemed like a younger,
boyish Declan. She blinked and lowered her eyes
quickly. The seduction scene wouldn't work on her
either! She'd had a taste of that and got her fingers
badly burnt. Maybe that was how he enticed his
women into his bed? She had to admit that for marks
out of ten he'd rate a definite twenty, but she knew
it wasn't for real even as her pulse-rate accelerated to
twice its normal speed. He was the original wolf!

'I'll do the dishes.' She marched out into the kitchen
with her head held high and her back straight.
Millicent was spending Christmas with her sister in
Devon and so she had the kitchen to herself. She leant
against the sink for a moment, looking out into the
stark, cold world outside which reflected exactly how
she felt inside. Naked, vulnerable, frightened . . .

After a few seconds she heard footsteps follow her
into the kitchen and turned quickly, intending to send
her mother back into the drawing-room while she

cleared away and loaded the dishwasher. Only it wasn't her mother's gentle warm face that looked back at her from the doorway. It was Declan's. And his face was neither warm nor gentle.

'Exactly what disease am I supposed to have?' he asked coldly as he piled an armful of crockery on to the work surface. 'And are you going to keep this up for the whole of the holiday?'

'What?' She stared at him stupidly as he opened the dishwasher and stacked the dirty crockery with an expertise that told her he had done this before.

'This freezing me out.' He moved closer to her, his voice low, and she noticed a touch of strain about the hard mouth. 'You haven't given me a chance to talk to you, to explain.' He shook his head abruptly. 'No, that's stupid. Not explain, to apologise.' There was a gruffness in his voice that spoke of embarrassment and she stared at him wide-eyed, disconcerted to see him less than fully in control.

'Apologise?' Her mind had gone blank. 'You've bought me a lovely Christmas present and I've given you nothing. It's I who should apologise.'

'Oh, to hell with the Christmas present!' He ground round on his heel and shut the kitchen door before facing her again, his eyes hooded now and his face sardonic. 'You know exactly what I'm talking about, Paige, so don't play dumb, it doesn't suit you.' His voice was acidly cynical.

'Oh, no?' The flame of anger he always seemed to ignite was flaring at full pitch now. He could even make an apology into a battle of wills! 'Well, maybe

I couldn't care less what you think suits me; have you considered that?'

'Paige!' Her name had been bitten out and now he took a slow deep breath, shutting his eyes for a second as though finding it all beyond him. 'I'm trying to tell you I was wrong, to ask your forgiveness. It wasn't the way you thought. Will you listen to me?' There was a strange expression on his face now which was threatening to melt her resistance and she took a step backwards, terrified she might succumb to the insidious attraction he had for her. She had to stop this!

'No.' She looked him straight in the face as she spoke and saw the shock of her rejection register for a second in the intent grey eyes. 'I don't want to listen to you, Declan, because I wouldn't believe a word you said.' Her hands were clenched fists and her slender body as straight as a ramrod as she faced him, and they stared at each other tightly for long seconds until he sighed deeply, his eyes rueful as he slowly shook his head.

'So young and determined,' he said quietly as his eyes ran over her face slowly. 'Don't you ever stop fighting, Paige? What is it that drives you?' He pulled her to him and she tensed stiffly, but he made no attempt to kiss her. Instead one hand stroked the back of her neck gently in a slow, rhythmic caress as his other arm settled her more securely against the hard bulk of his body. After a few moments she felt herself relaxing against him, the black silk of his shirt soft against her face and the clean, fresh smell of him encircling her with a sensual warmth. 'That's better.' There was a hypnotic, lazy quality in the deep husky voice that she had noticed before but was more pronounced now, producing a fluttering in her stomach that she recognised with a feeling of panic. She didn't want to respond to him, not now, not ever.

'How's Matthew?' His voice was soft against her hair and, lulled into a false sense of security by the dreamy, trance-like warmth that had settled on her mind and body, she answered without thinking.

'Matthew? All right, I think. I haven't spoken to him properly in weeks, I've been so busy.'

'Poor Matthew.' His voice was still quiet, but with a satisfaction in it that caught at her throat, and as he raised her head with his hand to look down into her eyes she saw that his face was hungry with desire. 'Happy Christmas, Paige...' This time she couldn't answer him as his mouth had taken hers in a long, deep kiss that seemed to draw the very essence of herself into him. She let herself fall into it, still in the chimerical, unreal mood his gentleness had induced, her senses swimming and the blood rushing thickly through her veins. It was happening again and, like before, she was powerless to stop it, this irresistible abandonment to all common sense and reason whenever Declan took her in his arms.

'I've missed you.' His voice was thick and low as he fitted her against his hard frame more closely, his tongue probing into the softness of her mouth in tiny little darts that sent a liquid heat flowing into her lower stomach. His hands were stroking her back now through the thin silk of her blouse, his fingers caressingly erotic as he kneaded her against him, and, like before, she was aware of his sensual expertise but unable to react against it. He seemed to know exactly how to touch her, to caress her, to turn her body into fire, and she felt helplessly excited as her head began to swim. As his hands reached beneath her blouse she tensed slightly, and then his voice whispered reassuringly against her ear. 'Relax, relax, it's all right.' All right?

It was as though those two words were catalystic in renewing the burning humiliation and hurt she had felt that afternoon in the summer. She jerked away from him as though he had burnt her, her eyes fiery and her face white. 'Leave me alone, Declan.' Her voice was a low hiss, but filled with such enmity that his eyes narrowed against it. 'I don't want you pawing me about.'

'Pawing you?' In other circumstances she could have laughed at the expression of almost comical horror and outrage that had turned his face black, but now laughter was the last thing on her mind. She glared at him in much the same way he was glaring down at her and then, after drawing a long, shuddering breath, he turned and left, shutting the door quietly behind him.

By the time she entered the drawing-room the kitchen was spick and span and she was quite composed, at least outwardly. She had heard voices as she cleaned the top of the stove but hadn't investigated, and now she saw to her relief that a few friends from the village had called by. Good. That would make the afternoon easier to get through. Less cosy.

'I think you know Margaret and Eric?' Gerald said as she smiled at the assembled company. 'And this is

Corinne and Bill, who are staying with them over
Christmas.' Introductions made, they all sat and
chatted for a few minutes and then Corinne, a pretty,
pert brunette in a scarlet jumpsuit, suggested they go
for a walk.

'I haven't done my aerobics this morning,' she
pouted with a slanted glance at Declan under her long
dark lashes, 'and I don't want to get fat after all that
Christmas pud Margaret heaped on my plate.' She
gave a little tinkle of a laugh that grated on Paige's
ears. 'I have to watch my figure, you know.' Her eyes
were melting on Declan's cool, amused face.

'A pleasant occupation.' Declan smiled lazily,
entering the conversation for the first time. He had
been standing to one side of the couples when she had
entered the room, his face closed and dark and his
eyes glittering as they had flicked over her pale face,
and now, as he dutifully responded to the pretty brunette's obvious request for flattery, a small dart of
pain pierced her heart region. It set the tone for the
afternoon.

Corinne was a shameless flirt and Declan had clearly
caught her fancy. The walk was a revelation to Paige
as to how far some women would go to get attention.
The little brunette laughed, teased, cajoled and
flattered Declan so outrageously that everyone seemed
to be taking it as a joke, including the man himself,
but Paige had caught the hard enquiring glances
Corinne had thrown at her when the others weren't
looking, and then the cat-like, slanted eyes had been
as cold as ice. She was clearly curious as to where

Paige fitted in the scheme of things, and especially the tenor of her relationship with Declan.

Paige gritted her teeth as she forced herself to remain outwardly calm and pleasant, seemingly relaxed, although the sight of Corinne hanging on Declan's arm at every opportunity was causing her stomach muscles to bunch in tight knots. There was blatant hot desire in the little brunette's eyes and if she could read it, Paige thought furiously, so could Declan. He knew exactly what Corinne was offering.

It shouldn't matter, Paige told herself again and again during the long walk, but for some reason it did, a lot. Every time the low affected giggle snaked into the cold air she felt physically sick, and once, when Corinne managed to elicit an amused chuckle from Declan at some ridiculous sally she had made, Paige found a white-hot emotion running through her she couldn't have named. She blessed the hard training of the 'ugly' years when she had become adept at maintaining a cool, proud front even when feeling wretched inside. It was coming into its own this particular day!

She could hardly believe any man would like such a brash, vulgar come-on but she had to admit, Corinne was undeniably sexy in her very cheapness. She couldn't resist glancing back once or twice at Bill to see how he was taking his wife's amazing behaviour, but he seemed quite unconcerned, deep in conversation with Gerald and Eric and seemingly quite unruffled by the outrageous mating display in front of him.

By the time they got home Paige's headache was a steady drumming throb at the back of her eyes and the nausea was a physical reality. She managed to get through the Christmas high tea that the others stayed for by sitting quietly at the back of the room with her head down and eating nothing, but when Corinne suggested a game of charades she decided enough was enough. Making her excuses, she fled up to the sanctuary of her room, accepting the hot-water bottle her mother brought a few minutes later with a grateful smile and then sinking into a deep, dreamless sleep almost immediately.

She hadn't glanced at Declan once since they had arrived home, although she had been painfully aware of every tiny movement he had made, and now, as the thick layers of sleep descended on her bruised mind and aching body, she was aware of wishing him into oblivion before sleep overtook her.

CHAPTER FIVE

WHEN Paige surfaced out of a thick, deep but strangely uncomfortable sleep the next morning she was conscious that the whole of her body was aching as though it had been stuck through with pins. Maybe it had, she thought idly, thinking of Corinne's small, sharp face. At least mentally. Her head was throbbing, her legs felt like lead and she longed to stay in bed, but the thought that Declan might think she was taking the easy way out and avoiding him goaded her into getting dressed.

Gerald, her mother and Declan were already in the breakfast-room when she opened the door, and as the odour of eggs and bacon assaulted her nostrils she took a silent deep breath, her face white. The smell of food was revolting.

'Don't you feel well?' her mother asked her with a troubled glance at her pale face as she quietly took her place at the table.

'Just a cold coming, I think.' Paige tried a smile but the effort was too much. 'I'll skip breakfast—just a cup of coffee, please.' The coffee tasted like dish-water and she could feel her cheeks and forehead beginning to burn even as she shivered in the warm air. She couldn't be ill. Not now. Not in front of Declan. Not when she needed to be strong and invincible.

'How about a piece of toast?' her mother asked anxiously after a few minutes. 'It might settle your stomach.'

'I don't mind.' Paige looked at the empty toast rack. 'I'll get some.' Her voice was dull and heavy.

'No, you sit there.' Her mother was half out of her seat but Paige had already left hers, walking on legs that suddenly seemed devoid of all feeling into the kitchen and placing two slices of bread in the toaster. When the door opened and then closed behind her she knew it was Declan. She had been conscious all the time she had sat sipping her coffee of his cool, expressionless face watching her intently, but had avoided meeting his eyes.

'When are you going to stop this childish behaviour?'

'What?' In her surprise she looked him straight in the face, her eyes puzzled. She had expected a word of sympathy, maybe a repeat of the apology of yesterday, but his voice was as cold as ice and his expression tight and angry.

'I said when are you going to stop this play-acting?' he bit out grimly. 'I can accept I'm not your most favourite person and I can promise you that in the future I'll make damn sure I'm not around at the same time as you visit, but couldn't you just try to make your mother's Christmas a pleasant one? She's looked forward for weeks to having you home, although exactly why defeats me! As spoilt brats go you sure take some beating.' He eyed her with searing disgust.

'Look, Declan——' He broke into her angry words as though she hadn't spoken and as she looked at his dark, cold face she was aware that she felt ill, very ill. She would have to sit down...

'I suppose you're going to skulk off to your room to avoid being with me?' he continued tightly. 'Well, what about Brenda? I hope this little act is fooling her, because it sure isn't fooling me, Paige. Paige?' As she began to fall she was conscious of the sudden change in his voice but she was past caring. A deep roaring blackness was coming up to meet her and she had no energy to fight it, sinking into the depths of a screaming darkness with a feeling almost of relief. She couldn't quite have lost consciousness because she was aware of Declan catching her before she hit the floor, and then his voice, sounding quite unlike him for once, calling for their respective parents. The rest was confused but still the real world. Declan carrying her to her room, her mother undressing her as though she were a baby, the room being clothed in semi-darkness and then the arrival of a stern doctor who mellowed slightly after examining her in spite of its being Boxing Day.

'This nasty flu that's about,' she heard him say in a loud whisper to her mother as he left the room. 'Coupled with the fact that she's obviously quite exhausted. Has she been overdoing the party life in the last few months?' She wished she had the strength to call him back and tell him exactly where he could stick the stethoscope that had been so cold on her hot skin, but she had to admit defeat. Her headache was blinding, her back was breaking and her mind was filled with cotton wool.

She slept all that day and the next in a daze of aching limbs, weird dreams and the endless drinks her mother presented at regular intervals, but in spite of it all the relief at not having to face Declan was paramount.

On the morning of the third day she awoke feeling a little more like herself. The grinding headache was gone and her brain was her own again; only a debilitating weakness remained in her limbs, which felt as though she had been stamped on by a herd of horses.

'Paige?' Her mother's look of relief as she came in to find her sitting up in bed after having tottered to the loo brought a feeling of guilt. What a Christmas! 'Are you feeling better?'

'Heaps,' Paige exaggerated quickly. In actual fact the short walk unaided to the *en suite* had brought home just how weak she felt.

'Not well enough to go out, though,' her mother said, plumping up her pillows as she stated the obvious.

'Go out?' She stared hard into the classical features so like her own. 'Of course.' She put a hand to her forehead. 'The theatre? Declan's treat. I forgot.' On Christmas Eve Declan had announced a joint Christmas present to them all of a trip down to London to the theatre and a first-class hotel overnight. And tonight was the night. Or wasn't, in her case. She couldn't stop a guilty feeling of relief that she had such a cast-iron excuse for not accompanying the others. 'I'm sorry, Mum,' she said in all honesty, 'I just don't think I could make it.'

'Of course not,' her mother agreed briskly. 'There's no question about it. We can go some other time.'

'Don't be silly.' The thought of twenty-four hours by herself was actually quite attractive. Much as she loved her mother, she was beginning to feel a little smothered by all the attention. 'You must all go. I can see to myself for goodness' sake; I'm over the worst now.' Her mother took a little convincing but was wavering as she left a few minutes later after depositing another inevitable cup of tea on the bedside cabinet.

Paige was surprised to find herself drifting back to sleep after a few minutes in spite of having done nothing else for nearly forty-eight hours, and when her mother came in later and whispered something in her ear she was aware of making what sounded like a sensible reply while missing the gist of the conversation. It was mid-afternoon when she surfaced again and immediately the quiet emptiness of the house homed in. They'd gone. She felt a small pang of she knew not what and tried to remember what her mother had said before she'd left. 'Fridge stocked——' she wrinkled her brow, and something '—was at hand.' She couldn't remember hearing the rest of that sentence. Never mind, she could fend for herself; she'd been doing it for years.

She climbed out of bed carefully, remembering the weakness of the morning, and was annoyed to find it was still with her, along with a peculiar swimming sensation in her head whenever she moved. She'd never had the flu before and realised for the first time how lucky she had been in the past. She felt sticky

Relax with FOUR FREE Romances plus two FREE gifts

Whatever the weather a Mills & Boon Romance provides an escape to relaxation and enjoyment. And as a special introductory offer we'll send you FOUR FREE Romances plus our cuddly teddy and a mystery gift when you complete and return this card. We'll also reserve you a subscription to our Reader Service which means you could go on to enjoy :

◆ **Six BRAND NEW ROMANCES** sent direct to your door each month.

◆ **NO EXTRA CHARGES** free postage and packing.

◆ **OUR FREE MONTHLY NEWSLETTER** packed with competitions (with prizes such as televisions and free subscriptions), exclusive offers, horoscopes and much more.

◆ **HELPFUL FRIENDLY SERVICE** from our Customer Care team on 081-684-2141.

> **Turn over to claim your FREE Romances, FREE cuddly teddy and mystery gift.**

Plus a FREE cuddly teddy and special mystery gift.

Reader Service
FREEPOST
P.O. Box 236
Croydon
Surrey CR9 9EL

Send NO money now

Free Books and Gifts claim

Yes Please send me four Mills & Boon Romances, a cuddly teddy and mystery gift, absolutely FREE and without obligation. Please also reserve me a subscription to your Reader Service; which means that I can look forward to six brand new Romances for just £11.40 each month. Postage and packing are FREE along with all the benefits described overleaf. I understand that I may cancel or suspend my subscription at any time. However, if I decide not to subscribe I will write to you within 10 days. Any FREE books and gifts will remain mine to keep. I am over 18 years of age.

2A4R

cuddly teddy   mystery gift

Ms/Mrs/Miss/Mr _____

Address _____

_____

_____ Postcode _____

Signature _____

and hot and uncomfortable and the thought of a bath was too good to resist. Her bedroom boasted a little *en suite* with a shower but the main bathroom on this floor had a sunken bath that was sheer luxury, and that was what she needed at the moment.

She glanced at herself in the mirror as she left the room, grimacing at her reflection dulled without her contact lenses. Tangled hair, pale face, mauve shadows under her eyes—what a picture! She was even more glad she had persuaded the others to go. She would die if Declan saw her like this.

As she stumbled along to the bathroom she found herself having to stop more than once to let her head rejoin the rest of her body, and by the time the water was running into the bath her heart was pounding as though she had run a mile and a strange feeling of disorientation was making her light-headed.

The mirror tiles covering the opposite wall showed a small bedraggled figure with huge eyes staring back at her under a mass of tangled red hair that made the white of her face even more startling by contrast. She'd wash her hair too. She nodded to herself as she shut her eyes for an instant. And then——

'What the hell do you think you're doing now?'

The shock of hearing Declan's voice right in her ear sent her toppling off the edge of the bath and into the foamy water, her nightdress and dressing-gown holding her down under the soft suds as she tried to surface. She was suddenly yanked, firmly and roughly, into a sitting position and opened dazed hazel eyes to see his furious face inches from her own. 'You're ill! You shouldn't be out of bed, let alone thinking of having a bath by yourself! Haven't you got a grain of sense?' It was as well he was holding her, because her limbs had turned to jelly.

'Stop shouting at me.' She tried to sound defiant but then spoilt the effect by suddenly bursting into loud, uncontrolled sobs which had the same effect on Declan as the sound of his voice had had on her, if the look on his face was anything to go by. He lifted her, dripping wet and shaking helplessly, into his arms, and sat holding her as he seated himself on the nearest thing, which happened to be the loo.

'Don't, Paige, don't cry,' he said softly as he reached for a large bath-towel behind him and wrapped it round her. 'I'm sorry, I shouldn't have shouted but you scared me half to death sitting there looking like the ghost of Christmas past. I thought you were going to pass out again.'

'I nearly did with you bellowing like that,' she said weakly as the sobs subsided into hiccuping gasps. 'I thought I was by myself; you shouldn't be here.' She tried to stand up but the hard arms holding her so firmly tightened and it was easier to give in to his strength than attempt to fight it. She couldn't have anyway; she felt as weak as a kitten.

'Your mother told me you knew I was staying, that you'd agreed,' he said quietly as he turned her to face him. She wished he hadn't. Sitting sideways as she had been, she hadn't been able to see his face, but now it was a breath away and he looked ... good. Whereas she looked like something even the cat wouldn't deign to drag in. 'I insisted they went to the show,' he continued softly. 'There was no need for us all to miss it and your mother needed a break.'

'Yes.' Her hair was dripping cold drops of water down her face, her sodden nightdress and dressing-gown was clinging to her in the most uncomfortable way and she was aware that she had soaked him too. 'I must have been dozing when she told me. I remember her coming in but that's all.' She stared at him miserably.

'Paige?' His voice was husky and for the first time since she had known him she saw he was struggling for words. 'The apologies are mounting up, aren't they? I'm sorry I didn't believe you were ill; I thought——'

'I know what you thought,' she interrupted quickly as she tried to rise again, and this time he let her go, his eyes filled with a dark watchfulness that made her breath catch in her throat. 'It doesn't matter...' She swayed slightly and steadied herself on the edge of the washbasin. 'Can I have a bath now?' she asked with a valiant attempt at composure which didn't sit well with the bedraggled state she was in.

'Don't be so ridiculous.' This was the Declan she knew, brusque, authoritative and as hard as nails. 'You can barely stand up.' He eyed her scathingly.

'I won't have to stand up in the bath, will I?' she said as reasonably as she could considering she felt like hitting him. 'I need a bath, Declan, and I must wash my hair now, it's wet anyway.' She looked at him pleadingly as his face remained closed. 'Please, I feel horrible.' Her bottom lip trembled.

He sighed impatiently as he stood up, glancing down at his trousers which were no longer immaculate. 'You really are the most...' His voice died away as she continued to keep her eyes fixed on him. 'Well, only if you agree to keep the door unlocked and allow me to stand sentry duty outside,' he said with a dark frown. 'If you faint again——'

'I shan't!' His suggestion had seemed faintly shocking although she couldn't quite fathom why. 'And there's no need for you to stand outside; I'll be all right.'

'I'm not a peeping Tom, Paige.' He seemed more amused than offended, his lips twisting in a wry smile. 'And I can assure you you haven't got anything I haven't seen before...many times,' he added for good measure, as a tinge of pink stained her cheeks.

'I don't doubt it for a minute,' she said sharply, glaring up at his cool face. 'But you haven't seen me and that's the difference!' The amused chuckle that accompanied his grin should have made her angry but again she caught a glimpse of that younger Declan that twisted her heart in some strange unaccountable way, and the danger signals were wailing shrilly in her head. He was dangerous, he was without principles, and she had better not forget it.

'Now be a good girl and do as you're told,' he said softly as he leant across and placed a light kiss on her nose. 'I'll be waiting outside. My old robe is hanging behind the door; you can use that when you get out.'

'I don't want——' But he had gone, shutting the door behind him as he left. For a moment she thought about defying him and locking the door, but then decided she didn't dare. He was quite capable of breaking the door down. He might have been smiling when he left but that hard square jaw spoke volumes.

She didn't linger in the warm silky water but felt altogether different when she opened the door ten minutes later swathed in Declan's towelling robe and with her hair wrapped turban-fashion in a small hand-towel. He was waiting, as promised, just outside, leaning lazily against the far wall with his hands thrust deep in his pockets. She saw he hadn't changed and the way the damp cloth moulded to the strong, powerful line of his legs and inner thighs suddenly made her feel quite hot.

'Now you dry your hair and get into bed while I bring you some toast,' he said firmly as he took her arm and walked her back to her bedroom a few feet away.

'Declan!' She shook his arm off as they reached the door and frowned up at him, her clean, scrubbed face glowing pink. 'I'm not an invalid! I'm going to get dressed and come downstairs, so you just fix your own meal and I'll get what I want in a minute.' She raised her chin defiantly even as her legs trembled.

'I'm not arguing with you, Paige.' The smile slid from his face to turn into a scowl that darkened his countenance alarmingly. 'I've been reasonable, I've allowed you liberties that were questionable, but now you do as I tell you. You've had a bad attack of flu made worse by being totally run-down in the first place, and you're obviously not capable of looking after yourself, so for the moment I'll do it! You get in bed and stay there for the rest of the afternoon.

You can get up this evening,' he added magnani-
mously as he turned her round and pushed her through
the open doorway, 'if, and only if, I consider you're
well enough.'

'You can't tell me what to do!' She spun round to
tell him exactly what she thought of him, but it was
a mistake. As her head began to swim she tried to
catch hold of the doorpost, but Declan was there in
an instant, gathering her into his arms as he swore
softly at her white face, his eyes dark with emotion.

'Dammit, Paige, if you weren't so ill I'd put you
over my knee and smack some sense into the place
where your brains are,' he said tightly. He strode into
her bedroom, depositing her on the bed with more
irritation than gentleness and looking around him
angrily. 'Where's your hairdrier?' he asked roughly.

She wanted to argue with him but she really was
feeling most peculiar again, so instead she pointed to
the far end of the wardrobe where her hairdrier
reposed on a small shelf. The feel of his fingers on
her head as he played the hot air over her mass of
silky red hair did nothing to deflect the dizzy, unreal
sensation that had her in its grip, and after he was
satisfied she could lie back against the pillows he stood
looking down at her with a grimness darkening his
austere features that made her flinch. He looked as
though he hated her.

'I'm sorry, Declan.' She suddenly felt very small
and very alone as she stared up into his face. 'I'm
being a nuisance, aren't I?' She gulped audibly. 'I'm
sorry,' she said again as she touched the sleeve of his

shirt in a little lost gesture. He stood quite still, looking down at her expressionlessly apart from a tiny muscle working in his jaw, and then removed her small hand from his arm.

'I know you think I'm made of stone, Paige,' he growled tightly through thin lips, 'but just at the moment I'm having the devil of a time trying to think of you as a sick woman. Now please——' he shut his eyes for an instant as he spoke '—just slide down under the covers and lie quiet before I get in there with you and do what I've been telling myself all morning I can't do.'

'Declan——'

'Shut up, Paige.' Ignoring her trembling voice, he cast one more furious look at her pale face surrounded by tumbling red hair that glowed like the sun and then turned and left, his big body stiff with control, returning a few minutes later with a tray containing two slices of buttered toast and a glass of freshly squeezed orange juice. He deposited the tray on her lap without speaking and taking great care not to touch her, and walked out again, his eyes narrowed and his expression saturnine.

Paige looked at the closed door helplessly as the tiny shivers that had been travelling up and down her spine since the admission of his desire began to lessen. What did all that mean? she thought weakly. She pictured his face as it had been when he'd last spoken and a tiny thrill flickered across her lower stomach. It didn't *mean* a thing, she told herself frantically as she still continued to stare vacantly at the closed door. He was a powerful, virile man used, no doubt, to a very active sex life. Of course, the . . . intimacy of the moment had got to him. She nodded to herself as she placed a piece of toast in her mouth automatically and began to chew. He didn't find her, Paige Green, as a *person*, attractive any more than any other woman in the same circumstances. He had proved that in the summer when he had been able to walk away from her without a moment's regret, whereas she . . . She wouldn't allow her thoughts to continue. He meant nothing to her and she was just another possible affair to him! No, she corrected herself painfully. Not even that. He hadn't wanted her that badly before; he had made that perfectly clear. They both knew that day in the copse would have had quite a different ending if he hadn't stopped when he had.

As her eyes began to sting with unshed tears she realised she had finished the toast, and after drinking the glass of orange juice snuggled down under the covers just as she was. She couldn't be bothered to get out of bed and find another nightdress. She was suddenly so tired that her limbs felt like lead . . .

It was dark when she awoke and she was aware straight away that she felt much better. She lay for a few minutes in the mauve darkness watching grey clouds scudding across the moon through the window, feeling warm and wonderfully relaxed. What had she been dreaming about? She tried to remember, but all that stayed with her was a sensation of pleasure and comfort. She was sure Declan had been in there somewhere. Declan! As the sound of his name in her mind brought her fully awake the events of the afternoon pressed in. What was the time? She glanced at her tiny alarm clock and saw it was nearly seven o'clock. He must be downstairs.

Should she get up? She swung her feet out of bed and, although a faint weakness remained, there was none of the dizziness that had proved so debilitating that morning. She dressed quickly in jeans, blouse and knee-length cardigan, looping her hair into a high ponytail and not bothering with even a touch of make-up, before quietly opening her door and walked silently downstairs on slippered feet.

The drawing-room was deserted, but the smell of cooking drew her to the kitchen, and as she opened the door Declan turned from the stove, his silver-grey eyes brilliant in the light from the fluorescent strip overhead and his face more dark than usual in contrast. 'Paige? What the——?'

As she looked at him she had the strangest feeling that he was surrounded by an aura of light and then he was at her side, almost lifting her into a chair and then looking down at her grimly. 'I told you to stay in bed!' She stared back at him silently as the dizziness receded.

'I feel much better,' she protested weakly. 'I was all right till I saw——' She stopped abruptly, aware that she couldn't really continue.

'Me?' he finished sardonically as he took a step backwards. 'Thank you *so* much. I do take it the feeling I inspired was not one of feminine weakness at my irresistible male charm?' He was joking at his own expense, she knew that, but he was a little too near for comfort if only he had known it, she thought grimly. And this feeling he inspired was crazy, ridiculous!

'Are you still that frightened of me?' he asked quietly as his voice took on a deeper tone. 'There's no need to be; I wouldn't do anything to hurt you.'

It was the ultimate in irony coming from him, and she lowered her head without replying, but not before he had caught the bitterness that twisted her mouth for a moment. There was dead silence for a few seconds and for the life of her Paige was unable to break it.

'Would you care for a glass of wine?' His voice was very cool, and as she glanced up she surprised a broodingly cloudy darkness in the grey eyes that was gone in an instant as he caught her gaze.

'Thank you.' She nodded her acceptance and he poured a glass from the half-empty bottle on the table, refilling his own glass as he did so.

'Steak and salad suit?' He turned to the stove to check the two juicy steaks sizzling under a very low grill. 'I thought it was time you ate, and of course I need to keep up my strength. But I don't need to tell you that, do I?' He was being deliberately provocative and she ignored the innuendo.

'Steak and salad sounds lovely,' she said carefully as she took a sip of wine. She had to be cool and calm, she *had* to.

'Good.' He expertly tossed the prepared salad in a big wooden bowl, adding oil and seasoning with a deft hand. There was an uncomfortable silence for a few minutes and Paige searched for a fairly bland remark to break it. Act normal, Paige.

'Do you like cooking?' she asked quietly.

He smiled grimly as he nodded. 'Doesn't fit in with your mental picture of me?' he remarked astutely. 'Well, much as I hate to disappoint that fertile little imagination, it so happens I do enjoy cooking. At home.' He noticed her raised eyebrows and continued. 'And, as you're wondering, I don't mean here. Home is a tenth-floor apartment in a high-rise in the middle of New York. Not everyone's cup of tea, but it suits me.' He smiled dismissively and she gathered that the brief glimpse into his private life was at an end.

'What sort of food do you prefer?' she asked cautiously, not wanting him to think she was giving him the third degree.

'Chinese.' He had his back to her now, turning the steaks again. 'But it's difficult to get the flavour just right. One little slip and the delicate flavour of a dish is ruined.'

'Oh.' She had that strange feeling again that these little revelations into his private life always induced. 'Have you learnt from a cookery book?'

He turned and eyed her for a moment, his eyebrows raised mockingly. 'Mostly, yes,' he said after a long moment, the twist to his mouth humorous. 'The sort of ladies I usually mix with are not the domesticated type.' The firm mouth hardened slightly. 'They expect to be wined and dined for their...companionship.'

The shaft of pain was piercing as his words registered and she dropped her eyes quickly, taking a sip of wine.

He didn't speak again as he busied himself getting plates and crockery set out on the scrubbed kitchen table, and it gave her time to warn herself, for the hundredth time this Christmas, to be careful. His charm was lethal, and never more so than when he was unaware of it, like now. The sight of him behaving in such a domesticated manner was doing crazy things to her equilibrium, presenting as it did a softer, more approachable side to his complex personality. But it was just one facet! She hammered the point home ruthlessly. There were no doubt others there just waiting to be discovered, but not by her! She made herself a mental promise. Definitely not by her, however tempting the idea might seem. And it did, just at the moment.

She couldn't describe this feeling that seemed to leap into urgent life when she was in his presence, but whatever it was it was very powerful, and by its very energy weakening to her. It was compounded of so many facets that she couldn't distinguish just one, but she recognised bitterness, anger, a strange, tender, painful yearning and, overall, a burning hot passion that still took her unawares with its intensity.

She *knew* he moved in a world where both sexes used each other for a time for sexual pleasure and then moved on to the next person without a shred of remorse or regret. She *knew* he could be ruthless, cold, that he was a clever, astute businessman surviving beautifully in the hard jungle of New York finance, and yet... There were those moments of vulnerability, of tenderness, and the affair of Jon and Tricia. He didn't add up at all. Or was she imagining that gentle side? Trying to make excuses for the way she felt?

She shivered suddenly, although the kitchen was warm. She couldn't let him affect her so violently, and this would have to be the last time she came to visit when he was here. She would have to make it clear to her mother and Gerald that her feelings for Declan were a thing apart for her love for them, and that she couldn't manage the anger, the aggress-iveness and still be someone she liked, and her self-respect was something very precious to her.

She stared at the broad masculine back as he bent over the stove, the dark shock of hair gleaming in the artificial light. He was too disturbing and she wouldn't question why. He was just too disturbing!

CHAPTER SIX

'Was that my excellent cooking or were you just famished after not eating for days?' Declan smiled down at her empty plate with a little flicker of satisfaction he couldn't hide.

'Both.' Paige smiled back carefully. 'I'll load the dishwasher and clear up.' She kept her voice cool with some effort.

'No way.' He pushed her back down in her seat as he passed. 'Sit still—you're ill, remember? And there's only a couple of plates; I'll wash them.'

As he turned to the sink, with his back to her, her eyes were drawn to his hair and she noticed a tiny wisp that had curled into his neck. For a startling moment it produced an inexplicable warm tenderness which absolutely terrified her. She *had* to pull herself together, *had* to get back to loathing the very ground he walked on, but suddenly he himself was getting in the way. How could she ever have thought of his face as harsh or tough? she asked herself distractedly. The danger of such thoughts sent a chill of fear racing down her spine and there was a frown on her face as she gazed at his broad back. It was the flu. She was still feeling the effects.

'Coffee?' He indicated the machine gaily gurgling away. 'You go through to the drawing-room—there's a fire there—and I'll bring a tray.'

'No, thank you.' She spoke quickly, too quickly, and as he turned to face her she saw that his face was tight with barely suppressed irritation.

'You're quite safe, Paige,' he said mockingly as his eyes swept over her troubled face. 'I'm not going to leap on you at the first opportunity, whatever impression I may have given you upstairs. Now go and sit down and I'll bring the coffee through.'

She stared at him helplessly for a moment and then rose without speaking to do as he said. She couldn't fight him and herself, not at this moment, and she *did* want, against all reason and logic, to sit with him in the quiet, peaceful room in front of the crackling log fire with the lights from the Christmas tree giving the room a soft, warm glow. She didn't know when she would see him again after this holiday-time, and suddenly each minute was painfully precious.

You're a fool, Paige Green, she told herself as she curled up in a big easy-chair, ignoring the settee close to the fire—a stupid fool. You're letting a physical attraction take you over. Because that was *all* it was, a transient, deceptive physical attraction. That was all it could be.

When Declan entered a few minutes later she saw the black eyebrows raise fractionally as he glanced at the empty settee, but his face was cool and expressionless as he settled the tray on a low coffee-table, although his very silence seemed to fill the room with tension. How could he say so much without uttering a word? she marvelled, and then glanced at him uncertainly as he gave a wry bark of a laugh.

'Comfortable?' The meaning was unmistakable, and she flushed violently before a dart of anger came to her aid.

'Perfectly, thank you.' There was a tight, stinging silence and then he relaxed visibly, reluctant amusement in his eyes as he patted the empty space beside him with a cursory hand.

'Come on, Paige,' he said smoothly. 'I've no doubt where I stand with you, you've made it abundantly clear, but this is taking things too far. I've no intention of calling across the room to you, so come and sit here like a good little girl and drink your coffee.'

Did he have any idea, any idea at all, what he did to her? she thought desperately—of the way he could send flickers of excitement down her spine with just the lift of a dark eyebrow? She hoped not, she did so hope not.

'Please?'

As her eyes opened wide he displayed his talent for seeing into her mind again. 'And you're quite right, I don't say please often, and certainly not in these circumstances.' The dark face was rueful. 'I can't remember when I had to persuade a female to sit by me.'

'Can't you?' She had tried for cool amusement but her voice was too shaky to carry it off and again the silver eyes narrowed on her face, their clearness piercing.

'Come on.' As he patted the seat again she rose slowly and seated herself gingerly next to him, shatteringly conscious of the lean, hard body beside her and of how he could make her feel without any apparent effort on his part. He was dangerous, he was *so* dangerous.

'Do you get tired of men telling you how beautiful you are?' They had been sitting watching the leaping scarlet and orange flames spark up the huge chimney as they sipped the coffee, and now, as his soft voice spoke in her ear, she had to force herself to show no reaction.

'Beautiful?' She turned slightly to face him, determined not to be ensnared by a lover's game. 'Beauty is skin-deep, Declan, and means different things to different people. It's unimportant.' There was no arrogance or false modesty in her tone, just a deep sincerity as she spoke the truth of the lesson she had learnt years ago.

'Unimportant?' The silver gaze was disturbingly intent. 'To most of the women I know it's everything. I can think of several who would sell their souls for such exquisite eyes and red hair.'

'Then I feel sad for them, because there's so much more,' she said quietly, turning to look into the fire again, the flames turning her hair into a glowing vibrant mass of red silk. 'I'm grateful that I'm not ugly, but in the last few years I've learnt that our Western world places too much emphasis on such things. When I see some of the pictures on TV of those starving children and the volunteers who spend their lives helping in desolate, out-of-the-way places, I'm ashamed I ever——' She stopped abruptly, horrified at what she had been about to reveal.

'Ashamed you ever . . . ?' His voice was curious.

'Ever thought good looks were important too,' she
said lightly after a long, taut moment. What would
he say if he knew that she had cried endless tears about
that very thing, craving beauty with a fierce determination only to find, when the ugly duckling
matured into a swan, that it was the lessons of life
she had learnt along the way that were most precious
to her. She had become her own person, content with
herself inside rather than concerned with the outward
shell. And it had happened without her even realising
it.

'There are few people who can surprise me these
days, Paige, but you are a constant revelation.'

As she turned to make a flippant remark to bring
the conversation out of the intimate mood it had fallen
into the words dried on her tongue. He was serious—
deadly serious, she saw, and the expression on his face
could only be described as tender.

'Sweet, funny, fierce, idealistic...' He shook his
head as he moved infinitesimally closer. 'Don't you
have a defence at all, a shell to protect you from all
the hurt the world can inflict? Don't you know that
caring about anything is the biggest trap of all?'

He had taken her mouth before she could reply and
then there was only sensation as he drew her into his
hard frame and she felt the shock of his arousal. His
breath was warm and pure as he covered her face in
tiny urgent kisses that lit a flame of wild excitement,
and as his mouth returned to her half-open lips she
heard herself moan with a feeling of helplessness. He
felt so good, so warm, so alive.

'You're like a drug to me, Paige, so help me...' His breath was a shuddering sigh against her hot cheek and there was a slow-growing heat inside her that was destroying the ability to think, to question. 'And this is madness...'

She shouldn't be allowing this. The thought was faint and weak as she felt his hands on her bare flesh where the front of her blouse had been expertly undone without her noticing, but as the lightly stroking caresses brought her arching against him the flickers of unease grew in time with her desire. She was just another woman to him, another easy conquest in his life, but unlike the others she wouldn't be able to walk away with a nonchalant smile once he had possessed her. How was she going to feel when that cold silver gaze looked at her without the light of passion to warm it, blank and chilling? He wanted her? Well, so he did; he had been home over a week— he probably needed a woman, *any* woman. She forced her mind to hold on to that thought as she writhed in his arms, pulling away before he could guess her intention.

'Declan, please... I don't want this... I can't...' For a panic-filled moment she thought he was going to reach out for her again as he stared at her in disbelief, his breathing harsh and ragged and his face dark with desire. 'I mean it,' she said desperately. 'You must stop.'

'I must stop?' His voice was incredulous as he took a deep, shuddering breath. 'But you were there with me, weren't you? I thought——'

Oh, yes, she knew what he had thought, and he wasn't far wrong, she acknowledged hotly, burning waves of humiliation sending the colour surging into her face as she covered her breasts with the open blouse. It was the summer all over again: he beckoned and she fell into his arms like an over-ripe plum! She was aware in some small part of her mind that she was whipping up her anger as defence against the trembling that seemed to have taken hold of her body, forcing rage and resentment past the other emotions that were so weakening, so traitorous.

'What gives you the right to think you can treat me like...like...?' She couldn't find the words to express herself properly, but Declan's face hardened as he took in her accusing eyes and now it was he who placed space between them, rising abruptly and striding halfway across the room before swinging to face her again, his mouth a thin white line.

'I thought I was treating you like a woman, Paige, a beautiful, desirable woman who wanted——'

'Wanted what?' she interrupted him shrilly as a mixture of self-disgust and anger turned her eyes brilliant. 'You think you're irresistible, is that it? That I should be grateful to stand in line with all the others?'

'Now just a damn minute!' He didn't move a step towards her but the force of his anger reached out with icy-cold sharpness. 'I've never yet made love to one woman when I'm involved with another one and I sure as hell wouldn't start with you! I don't know what little fantasies that imaginative mind of yours has spun but I wasn't trying to seduce you for some twisted pleasure—and I'm as free as a bird, incidentally. Can you say the same?' The last words were aggressively hostile and for a moment she stared at him blankly before the realisation that he was talking about Matthew cut through her consciousness. She opened her mouth to make a vehement repudiation of the unspoken charge, but even as the words hovered on her tongue she bit them back. She would leave this little scenario with dignity even if it killed her.

'I'm going to bed.' She rose with immense hauteur which dissolved in a flash at his cruel laugh.

'Do I take it that is not meant as an invitation?'

He could joke, he could actually *joke* at such a time as this? 'You're despicable.' The words were flat and empty and for a moment the harsh face in front of her froze as though her words had hurt him, which of course was impossible. Ice had no feelings.

'So? I'm despicable.' He repeated her words with frightening calm. 'I really don't know what's the matter with you, Paige,' he continued in the same chillingly conversational tone of voice, 'but I'm getting a little tired of being made to feel like the original Marquis de Sade.'

'The matter with *me*?' The injustice was too painful to ignore. 'I suppose that day in the summer was a figment of my imagination, is that it? It never happened?'

'I wondered when we would get round to that,' he said tightly. 'I've apologised—what more can I do?'

But she didn't want an apology, she thought with sad, desperate fury. Words were cheap. She wanted him to *care* that he'd hurt her, *care* that for years he

had shut her out of his life, *care*—— Her own mind
banged a door firmly shut before she went any further.
'Yes, you apologised,' she agreed emptily.

'That afternoon took me by surprise just as much
as you,' he said quietly after a long, taut moment of
silence. 'I had intended that we get to know each other,
that was all, maybe build a foundation of friendship
for the future.'

She wished with all her heart that she could believe
him, but to do that would mean a leap of faith that
was impossible. He was confusing her again, she
thought vaguely, twisting events to make black white
and white black.

'Paige? Can we talk about it?'

It was all a trick, she thought wildly, that uncertain, haunted, questioning look in his eyes. She
wouldn't be fooled by this man again. He had hurt
her twice, deeply, she couldn't be naïve enough to
allow it to happen a third time. 'There's no point,'
she said wearily, pushing back her heavy mane of hair
with a shaking hand. 'I don't want to talk about anything with you, Declan.'

'And that's the final line?' The light grey eyes with
their silver light were blank now; he had donned that
mask he wore so well. 'No reprieve?'

'I don't trust you,' she said with devastating
honesty. 'I can't.'

'The hell you can't!' The iron control was slipping;
she could sense it although the dark face betrayed no
emotion. 'You *won't*—that's different.'

'I'm not bandying words with you.' The piercing
gaze held her pinioned, although every instinct in her

body was telling her to leave. There was something in the deep, rasping voice that was terrifying.

'Maybe talking won't get us anywhere,' he agreed softly as he moved to stand in front of her. 'You might despise and hate me, but we both know there's something between us that can render all your objections useless in the space of minutes.'

'You mean sex?' she said baldly, trying to break the intimacy that had her longing to rest her head against that broad chest while his mouth covered hers. 'Is this the line you give all your women?'

'Stop it, Paige.' The words were ground out savagely through clenched teeth. 'Stop fighting me. I can't tell you I'm Little Boy Blue because it wouldn't be true and we both know it. I work hard and I associate with men and women of like mind who enjoy their work and have little time for romantic liaisons that cost time and effort. The women I've known were looking for a good time with no strings attached and I appreciated them as they appreciated me. That was all there was to it. No heartache, no broken dreams. I'm sorry if that disappoints the image you have of me as a wrecker of lives, but it's the truth.'

'That's very sad.' She stared at him, her eyes enormous. 'Very sad and very wasteful. What are you going to do one day, Declan, when you wake up to find you are an old man with nothing to remember that means anything, nothing to hold on to——?'

'I don't need to hold on to anything,' he said violently. 'Can't you get it through your head that I'm happy? I planned my life this way—it's good, for crying out loud. I've got everything I want.' There was a deep huskiness in his voice that belied his words and a look in his eyes that made her want, against all reason, to take him in her arms and make love to him. 'And don't look at me like that,' he finished savagely.

'Like what?' Her voice was a soft little whisper but it seemed to inflame him still more.

'As though I need your sympathy,' he spat angrily. 'I can take the dislike, even the contempt, but never pity——'

The assault on her mouth couldn't be termed a kiss; it was hard and angry and fierce as he jerked her against his body. She had been aware of the muscled power in his big frame but she was experiencing its full strength now as she found herself utterly unable to move. Her head was forced back at a painful angle against the hard line of one arm and her body pinned tight as he crushed her to him, and as blind panic took over she began to struggle, but it was as ineffectual as the fluttering of a tiny bird in the jaws of a wolf.

The iron control had broken and his strength combined with her recent illness and slender build rendered all resistance useless; he didn't seem even to notice her struggles. He was under the influence of something beyond mere passion, a rage, an anger gripping his being that she felt was directed at himself as much as her.

The punishing kiss continued relentlessly until she thought her neck would break, and then, when she least expected it, the tempo of his anger changed, mellowed. She became aware that the hard mouth plundering hers had become coaxing, erotic, and as his hands loosened their steel hold on her softness his fingers stroked her lightly with featherlike caresses that brought the blood pounding through her veins. She wasn't aware of his hands on her body, just the sensations they produced as a whole, turning her limbs to water and blurring her mind until she was floating, drowning...

And then she was free. Abruptly, shockingly he moved away, leaving her swaying in the middle of the room like a slender reed in the midst of a storm.

'What am I doing?' The expression on his face froze her blood as he shook his head in much the same way a boxer did after the final knock-out blow. 'This isn't what I want...'

Paige couldn't think. Speech, sense had all dried up into a huge barren void. She had brought this third rejection on herself, she had. It was the only coherent thought in her head. She should have been stronger.

He had left her before she realised his intention and she was still staring after him moments later in the quietness of the still room as her mind struggled to come to terms with what had happened, and then, painfully, the nerve-endings that had been cauterised by shock began to hurt slowly.

'This isn't what I want.' The words were burnt into her soul. He didn't want *her*; he couldn't have said it any plainer.

The night was long and crucifyingly painful as her tired mind searched for sleep. She must have dozed off towards dawn, because it was light when she opened her eyes to the sound of the wood pigeon calling its velvet notes into the white winter sky, perched on the bare branches of the gnarled old lilac tree that grew beneath her window.

The reflection that stared back at her from the mirror was pale and agonised, and as her eyes travelled over the white face, red-rimmed eyes and bruised lips a flood of angry self-respect came to her aid. She would not be crushed by this thing, she wouldn't let herself undervalue her own worth as she had all night, or else all those lessons she had learnt in the past would count for nothing.

After a long hot shower she dressed carefully in white trousers and browny red jumper that exactly matched the colour of her hair, fastening long, swinging gold hoops into her ears and applying careful make-up to hide the ravages of the night. She left her hair loose, teasing its fullness into soft curling waves round her face, and by the time she had finished all the careful preparations she looked good.

It gave her the courage she needed to leave her room and walk downstairs as though she hadn't a care in the world. It felt like the hardest thing she had ever done.

She had cried all the tears she had to cry during the long night and now all that remained was the desire to get through this day, until Declan left, with the maximum of controlled aplomb and the minimum of thought. She had found that where he was concerned thought weakened her, and today she needed to be strong. Very strong.

The kitchen was empty but he had obviously been down at some point after she had left last night. The plates and cutlery had been put away, the work surface tidied and cleaned and the chairs neatly placed under the table. Everything looked bright and clean and normal in the white light streaming in from the cold winter's day outside.

Paige was cooking scrambled eggs on toast when Declan entered the kitchen some time later, not that she felt like eating, but the need to prove to him that she did was all-important.

She heard a slight sound behind her and turned quickly without thinking, her heart hammering into her mouth as she took in the big dark figure standing quietly in the doorway.

'Good morning.' His voice was deep and cool and he looked dreadful, she thought in the split-second before she turned away. He looked as though he hadn't slept all night, but that was ridiculous. He would have slept like a baby.

'Good morning.' She was relieved to find her voice obeyed her mind and not her emotions. 'Would you like some breakfast?'

'Breakfast?' It was as though she had just asked a question in a foreign language from the note of uncertainty in his voice, she thought numbly. 'No, just coffee, if it's not too much trouble. But first . . .' He walked over to her and turned her round to face him gently, dropping his arm immediately he had done so and stepping back a pace. 'This has been one hell of a Christmas for you, hasn't it, one way or another?'

She blinked but said nothing, steeling herself to stand absolutely still as he looked down at her, his face drawn and set.

'All I can do is to promise you that I will stay out of your life, whatever that takes.' She nodded slowly and he raked back his hair with his hand. 'If it's any consolation, which I'm sure it isn't, no woman has ever made me lose my temper the way I did last night.' His face was distant now, the small pulse beating tightly in his throat the only live thing in a face of granite. 'It was as much as a shock to me as it was to you.'

'I doubt it.' She had never expected to see a glimmer of light at the end of the tunnel during the long night, but somehow the combination of his obvious remorse and less than devastatingly cool appearance, combined with the glimmer of amazement at his actions that he couldn't quite hide, had ignited a faintly hysterical nervous amusement deep inside her. What a terrible, hopeless, unbelievable mess, she thought shakily as she turned back to the eggs, fighting back hot tears.

She forced the breakfast past the lump in her throat as he sat and drank his coffee silently, remembering, with a little twist to her heart, the steak and salad meal of the night before.

'How are you feeling?' he asked distantly as she rose to take her plate to the sink.

'Fine, thank you.' Again that nervous laughter threatened to erupt. Here they were, talking over breakfast so politely when only last night she could have ended up in his bed, if fate and Declan hadn't decreed otherwise.

'I shall be leaving about three this afternoon, by the way,' he said stiffly as she kept her back to him, watching a small fat robin digging enthusiastically for a worm in the little patch of dirt beneath the window. 'My father led me to understand that they'll be back about teatime so you won't be alone tonight.'

Paige nodded but didn't speak, and after a minute she heard him push back his chair and leave the room. She glanced over to the empty coffee-cup on the kitchen table and as she walked over and reached out for it the faint fragrance of his aftershave caused her stomach muscles to clench. What was it about him that even now, after all that had happened, culminating in that painful scene last night, he could affect her so strongly? She closed her eyes as she stood there, hearing a little flurry of raindrops spatter against the kitchen window. She should know better by now. He was the original wolf who walked alone, and yet there was another Declan she had caught the odd glimpse of now and again who was devastatingly different. Wasn't there? Or was it her imagination?

She sat down on the seat he had vacated and thought about the conversation she had had in the summer about him with her mother as her mind whirled and spun in confusion . . .

'Declan?' Her mother's voice came back to her as though she were sitting there in the kitchen. 'Oh, Gerald's quite given up expecting any hope of grandchildren from him!' Brenda had laughed ruefully. 'Love them and leave them seems to be Declan's policy. He's quite honest about the fact that his heart is never involved in his relationships—lays it on the line, so I understand. Gerald can never understand why they come back for more, but I suspect my

husband is a little chauvinistic in that respect. He can't
envisage that Declan's attitude suits some of those
women down to the ground, and besides, he's a
challenge . . .'

Paige nodded to herself now as the memory of her
mother's words faded away. The unattainable. Yes,
she could see how the women Declan moved with
would want that. They were mostly either determined
career women or rich and bored, and either way the
challenge, coupled with the enigmatic charm and cold,
hard mastery of his emotions, would be irresistible.

She was still sitting there an hour later, musing over
a fresh pot of coffee, when the shrill chimes of the
doorbell interrupted her thoughts. She heard the
murmur of voices in the hall, then a high shrill giggle
that she recognised with a bite of irritation. Corinne!
What on earth did she want? The absurdity of the
question hit her immediately. She knew exactly what,
or whom, the lovely brunette wanted! Was her
husband with her? She couldn't hear anything now
and longed to go and investigate, but the thought that
Declan might think she was interested in his relationship with Corinne stopped her.

A second later his dark head popped round the
door, followed by Corinne and then Margaret and
Eric. 'Hello.' Paige smiled brightly at them all without
letting her eyes rest on Corinne's smooth face a second
longer than she had to.

'Margaret, Eric and Corinne are walking into the
village for a pub lunch,' Declan said expressionlessly.
'They wondered if we'd like to come.' His face was
masterfully bland.

'Only if you feel up to it,' Corinne said quickly. 'We heard you caught the dratted lurgy like poor Bill. He's in bed now and positively dying.' She giggled lightly as though it were the funniest thing in the world. 'I suppose you're still feeling under par; you look a little peaky.' The hard, slanted gaze moved insultingly over Paige's face. 'We'll take Declan off your hands for a couple of hours if you like, let you have a little snooze.' She smiled dismissively, her eyes cold.

It was such an outrageously obvious and well-engineered exercise by Corinne to sink her talons deeper into Declan that for a moment all Paige could do was to stare at the other woman, her hazel eyes wide with a mixture of amazement and disgust. None of the others seemed to be affected in the same way. Margaret and Eric's faces were carefully blank and Declan was leaning lazily against the wall, his hands deep in his jeans pockets and his eyes narrowed and distant. They fastened on her now as her gaze flicked on to him and just for a moment she thought she saw the distaste she was feeling mirrored in the cool grey eyes, but then he blinked and turned away and the impression died. Corinne was his type of woman, after all.

'Well, Paige, do you want a "little snooze"?' he asked blandly as he levered himself off the wall, his whole demeanour stating quite clearly that it was of no importance to him what she decided. She saw the glint of delight in Corinne's hungry eyes.

'Not particularly.' She smiled coldly straight into Corinne's disappointed face. 'And after you've been kind enough to come and call, I wouldn't dream of not joining you. Should we call in on your husband first and see if he needs anything?' She saw the none too subtle reminder of her married status register in Corinne's stony brown eyes with a feeling of satisfaction. The others might be happy to go along with the small brunette's unsavoury and highly questionable conniving, but she was blowed if she was! You're a cheap little flirt, Corinne, she thought silently as she stared back into the hard eyes. You know it and I know it.

'No need.' Corinne answered her question with a sharp flick of her dark head. 'He's asleep; he'll be asleep for hours.' She laughed lightly as she turned to Declan. 'That's one of the few things he does really well.' The dark eyes asked him to join in her mockery, but Declan gave her a long, straight look that made Corinne's head drop and her cheeks flush as she swung round to the door abruptly. 'Come on, then,' she said shrilly. 'I'm longing to stretch my legs.'

'Corinne is a keep-fit instructor,' Margaret said to no one in particular as they left the kitchen and walked into the spacious hall. 'She likes to keep active; I've lost count of all the sports she does.'

'Really?' There was a note in Paige's voice that expressed her opinion of the brunette perfectly and made Corinne swing back to glance piercingly at her face. Paige looked back at her innocently, her hazel eyes wide and open and her face composed. 'And does your husband play with you?'

'What do you mean?' Corinne's eyes were vicious.

'I think Paige was asking if your husband shares your enthusiasm for keeping fit,' Declan said smoothly into what had suddenly turned into a highly charged atmosphere.

'Not really.' Corinne shot her a last baleful look as they slipped on their coats. 'He runs his own business; that takes most of his time.' The cold eyes turned a shade warmer as they fastened on Declan. 'Besides, he isn't very good at any of the sports my health club offers, and the standard is very high. He came a few times but he just got in the way.' The gaze moved down Declan's body and then back up to the expressionless face. 'Now *you'd* be a big hit there.' Corinne's small pink tongue came out to lick her lower lip in a predatory cat-like gesture that made Paige feel slightly sick. 'A really big hit.'

'That's reassuring.' Declan looked down at the small woman wryly, his face satirical and openly mocking. 'But what if I failed my entrance exam?'

'You wouldn't.' Corinne fairly purred with satisfaction at the way the conversation was going. 'I'd make sure of that.'

As they all stepped out into the damp icy air Paige shivered before she could stop herself. After a few days of being entombed in the warm, centrally heated house the cold took her breath away for a moment.

'Here.' She glanced up in surprise to see the scarf Declan was holding out to her. 'Wrap up warmly, it's colder than you think,' he said brusquely.

'I'm all right really——'

Declan cut off her words as he placed the scarf round her neck, tucking the ends into the front of her

coat with a faintly mocking air that wasn't lost on
Corinne, standing watching them with narrowed eyes.
Paige steeled herself not to flinch as his warm hands
touched her throat but the stiffening of her body
communicated itself nevertheless, and his face was
grim as he turned back to the others.

They walked through the fields to the pub in a
laughing group and Paige was aware that she was
acting as she'd never acted before. Corinne didn't miss
an opportunity to further her cause with Declan,
pretending to stumble as they walked and catching
hold of his arm in a helpless little gesture that made
Paige's teeth clench, and then feigning a slightly
wrenched ankle that had her holding on to his arm with
octopus-like tightness as she repeated her performance of Christmas Day.

It was pathetic, it was obvious and altogether embarrassing, Paige thought hotly as she plodded along
on Declan's other side with Margaret and Eric on her
left, but Declan seemed to be enjoying every minute!
She glanced at him from under her eyelashes as he
chatted to Eric over her head. His face was cool and
enigmatic and quite unruffled even as Corinne decided her hands were cold and thrust the one that had
been holding on to Declan into his big coat pocket.

'You don't mind?' She smiled prettily, arching her
eyebrows.

'Feel free.' There was something in the mordant
voice that made Paige look more keenly, but his face
was veiled against her, set in the smooth, bland mask
that he did so well. It stayed in place throughout the
rest of the morning as they enjoyed a pre-lunch drink

and then feasted on the home-made beef soup and shepherd's pie that the landlady smilingly served. He treated Corinne with a kind of cynical unconcern that had the little brunette fairly turning cartwheels in an effort to make an impression, but parried all her attempts to draw him out with an expertise that made Paige suspect he had found it necessary to perfect the cold, suave evasiveness in the past.

Did he know how attractive the technique was? She glanced at him now as he sat idly leaning back in his chair in relaxed contemplation of the others, his dark face cool and collected and the silver-grey eyes slightly narrowed. Probably, she thought bitterly. One thing was for sure: she didn't have a clue as to what made his mind tick, whereas he, on the other hand, was handling Corinne with a deftness that indicated that women were no mystery to him. The idea was curiously painful.

The walk home in the early afternoon was a repeat of the morning's embarrassing performance but this time Paige purposely strode in front, with Margaret and Eric leaving Declan to Corinne's tender ministrations. She found she was boiling with anger, on automatic pilot as she held a conversation with the other two, her stomach squeezed into a giant knot and her head swirling with furious insults she would love to shoot into Declan's cool, contained face. But she had no right to do that, had she? The little voice in her head that was always blatantly honest reminded her coldly and dispassionately that Declan was a free agent, a grown man of thirty or so, quite capable of making his own decisions about life and love.

But someone else's wife? she argued silently to herself as she smiled at some obscure joke Eric was telling her. *That* was what was making her mad, nothing else. Nothing else? The little voice pecked away at her again as Corinne's throaty giggle behind them had Paige wishing for a machine-gun. Definitely nothing else, she answered firmly. She had been put in her place by an expert last night and it was a lesson she would rather forget. Declan meant nothing to her, absolutely nothing! The rugged, attractive face, piercing silver-grey eyes, big, aggressively male body— all left her stone-cold! That occasional boyish expression that could turn back the years as though he were a teenager, the faintly vulnerable uncertainty of his mouth this morning—no! She dragged her mind back from the path it was following ruthlessly. It all meant nothing! It *had* to mean nothing. The price she would have to pay for it to mean anything else was too monstrously high.

CHAPTER SEVEN

'WE WON'T stop for coffee, thanks.' Corinne blithely ignored the fact that she hadn't even been asked. 'But how about dinner tonight? Margaret has catered for four and poor Bill won't be around. Oh, Paige can come too, of course.' The slanted eyes flicked innocently in Paige's direction after having made the point that four was company and five meant smaller rations!

'Have to count me out, I'm afraid,' Declan said easily into the sharp little face looking up at him. 'But maybe Paige is free?' His voice was coldly dismissive, the meaning quite clear.

'Please, Declan.' There was no pretence of subtlety now as Corinne faced him and Paige knew a moment of deep humiliation for the other woman at such a total lack of pride. Margaret and Eric obviously shared her embarrassment as they shifted uneasily a few steps along the path, their eyes averted.

'I shan't be in the country, Corinne.' Declan's voice held no warmth at all, but Paige couldn't see his face. They were standing at the top of the blowy wind-swept drive in a small group and now, as Margaret and Eric continued to edge away, Paige began to walk towards the house without a backward glance. She hadn't bothered to refuse the dinner invitation—they all knew for whom it had been intended—and she had stood all she intended to take.

133

By the time she had fitted her key into the lock Declan was behind her, and as she turned she saw his face was as hard as granite. She glanced back, but the end of the drive was empty except for a rush of swirling brown leaves stirred up into a crazy mad dance by the cold wind. 'No Corinne?' she asked sarcastically as they stepped into the hall. 'Don't tell me she's given up as easily as all that.'

Declan shrugged powerful shoulders in a casual gesture that irked her unbearably, more so as he prepared to march upstairs without replying to her taunt. Her anger flamed hot.

'Well?' She knew she was going to regret this little confrontation, but wild horses couldn't have stopped her. 'Has she persuaded you to stay? Used her well-practised charms to entice the ice man out of his lair?'

'OK, Paige, spit it out.' He turned at the foot of the stairs, his eyes narrowed slits of light. 'You've been angling for this all day; let's have it all.'

'I'm just surprised at the type of woman you find attractive,' she said coldly as her eyes shot sparks. 'Today was the sort of display that I'd only seen before in third-rate movies of the more pathetic kind.'

'Is that so?' He folded his arms as he leant back against the wooden pillar of the stair rail. 'You go in for that type of film?' His voice was deadly calm.

'She's married, Declan.' The cool control was incredibly galling. 'Don't you care about that?'

'It's nothing to me if she's married or not,' he said expressionlessly. 'Why should it be?'

'Why *should* it be?' Her voice was an unattractive screech and she took a deep breath before she spoke again, her cheeks burning hot. 'Isn't there anything that means something to you, Declan? Anything at all?'

'Don't push it.' Her insult had turned the silvery eyes nearly black with rage. 'I'm reminding myself at the moment that I owe you after last night, but I can only be pushed so far. Take care.'

'Take care!' She repeated his words with biting contempt. 'What will you do if I don't? Force me into submission again using brute force? You're good at that, aren't you?'

He gave her one long look that burned with constrained rage and then turned again to walk up the stairs.

'You still haven't answered my question,' she said loudly, and as he paused with one foot on the bottom step she saw his body stiffen as though he was bringing every muscle under iron control. 'Are you staying?'

'No, I am not staying,' he said with exaggerated patience.

'You're not availing yourself of the warmth of Corinne's bed?' she said with hard mockery. 'You *do* surprise me.'

'Obviously.' He faced her again now and she saw to her amazement a kind of pain mixed with the biting anger that suddenly cut through her rage like a hot knife through butter. What was she doing? she asked herself frantically. Why had she let jealousy turn her into the sort of woman she despised, worse even than Corinne? Jealousy? As the revelation hit her mind she jolted with shock. She wasn't jealous! Never. Not of Declan! 'But then, I constantly surprise you, don't

I, Paige? Wicked, ruthless Declan without a decent bone in his body!' His words pierced the sense of horror that had her in its grip as she stared at him wide-eyed and open-mouthed.

'I am not responsible for the ideas that Corinne and women like her dream up,' he said icily. 'Her fantasies are her own concern and as far as I'm concerned that is exactly what they'll stay: *fantasies*. I find her attitude . . . distasteful.'

'You expect me to believe that?' she asked faintly.

'I don't expect you to believe a damn thing, Paige,' he said tiredly, 'and just at this moment I don't care either. This holiday has been less than enjoyable for me, and frankly all I want to do is to get back to my own world. Is that plain enough for you?' His eyes bit into her white face. 'No Corinne, no anybody! OK?'

'If that's the way you want it.' She brushed a stray strand of hair off her face with a shaky hand as the pain bit deep.

'The way I want it?' His harsh bark of a laugh made her jump violently. 'What does the way *I want* things have to do with anything where you're concerned?'

There was something working in the darkness of his face she didn't understand, and she fell back on her mother's words as a kind of talisman against the doubt that was beginning to sear her mind with sickening uncertainty. 'But you live your life exactly how you want to,' she said slowly. 'Independent, free, affairs one after the other. You like your women to be——'

'Since when were you an authority on the type of women I like?' he asked furiously. 'You know nothing about me! Nothing! Hell, I'm a grown man of thirty. Do you seriously expect that I've been celibate since puberty?'

'Of course not.' She answered him in the same vein now. 'But there's no need to be so...' She stopped, unable to find the right words.

'Yes?' His eyes were murderous. 'Please go on.'

'So shallow!' She glared at him angrily. 'All right, maybe you wouldn't have an affair with a married woman, but you always make sure you have no ties, no commitments with the women you *do* choose, don't you? Deny it! You can't, can you? You can't!' She shook her head heatedly. 'You say you want to go back to your world but it isn't real, up there on your tenth floor where no one can touch you, where it's all make-believe!' She didn't know how to explain what she felt; it was all tumbling out in a confusion of incoherent words that sounded like the ramblings of a mad woman. 'You fly from continent to continent, mix with the right people, always on the move, but what does it all mean——?'

'It means conducting my life the way *I* want it,' he said harshly. 'A basic human right, I think you would agree?'

'No, I wouldn't,' she shot back sharply, 'not when it's a case of being scared to take a risk.'

'Scared to take a risk?' His face was incredulous. 'I wouldn't have got to where I am now if I were frightened to back my hunches. I've lost some money in my time but——'

'Money?' She moved to stand in front of him, her small chin stuck out aggressively and her face tilted up to his. 'I'm not talking about money! I'm talking about life, Declan! Caring for someone whatever it takes, being there in the good and bad times, putting someone else before yourself even when it hurts, even when it's unfair. Marriage, families, growing old together—that's what I'm talking about.'

'Why?' He stared at her blankly. 'Why are you talking about that?'

'Because that's what it's all about!' She almost screamed the words at him. 'If you haven't got that you haven't got anything at all, can't you see? Real life isn't a hundred per cent certain. You can get hurt, badly, but that's a chance you have to take. You're opting out, Declan.'

'Too damn true!' There was a starkness, a bitter hardness in his face that cut off her words like a knife. 'You like real life?' He took her arm and shook her slightly. 'I'll give you real life, honeypot. My mother married my father when she was sixteen and he was a boy of nineteen and she regretted it within six months, but by then it was too late.'

'Too late?' she asked faintly as his fingers bit into her arm. The mask was off now; she was seeing the real Declan, and it frightened her.

'Much too late,' he said grimly. 'I was already on the way and so she was trapped, committed. Or at least that was the way she saw it. There was no question of an abortion or separation for her once she knew she was carrying a new life, and besides, she thought my father loved her.' The last three words were spoken with such bitterness that she hardly dared breathe as the darkness emanating from him enveloped her.

'She told me all this when she was dying, to try and warn me to live life to the full and not tie myself down in a relationship until I was sure it was the right one. She said my father had been a good husband, life had been...adequate.' He breathed deeply, his eyes looking back into the past now and blind to her face lifted up to his. 'The fact that she was sure he loved her so much was some consolation for the wasted years, the sacrifice of living with a man she didn't love, and of course she cared very deeply for me. And then she was gone, her life snuffed out at thirty because she didn't have the will to live.'

'But it was her heart,' Paige protested softly. 'My mother said——'

'That was what was written on the death certificate,' Declan said coldly, 'but there was no joy, no fulfilment in her life, and that is death to the soul. Exactly three months after the funeral my father went out on his first date with an old neighbour and from that time on he was rarely without a woman. That was this great love my mother had thought he had for her.' His eyes were cloudy with remembered pain and bitterness and Paige's heart lurched as she thought how the boy Declan must have suffered at his father's apparent shallowness. And she had called *him* shallow! 'He married your own mother after having known her just a few weeks, and this was the man my mother had sacrificed her life to. You tell me,

Paige,' he added suddenly, his face savage. 'You tell me what real love is!'

'Declan ...' She stared into the dark face for a moment, lost for words, and as he stared back into her wide eyes he seemed to come back to himself, the sardonic mask that hid the real Declan slipping firmly into place.

'So.' He smiled stiffly as he released her arm and took a step backwards. 'Now you know.'

'I'm sure you've got this all wrong.' Her brow wrinkled as she tried to formulate her thoughts. It was suddenly imperative that she touch that inner man, the one that was still hurting so badly after all the years. 'It wasn't that Gerald didn't love your mother the way she thought; he didn't marry again for years and years, did he? It's just that he's the sort of man who can't be without a female companion; it was no reflection on your mother or the way he felt about her.'

'What do you know about it?' he said caustically as his face hardened still further. He was bitterly regretting letting his guard down; she could feel it, see it in the icy glittering eyes.

'Plenty.' She ignored the scorn in his voice. 'I've got to know your father very well over the years and he's just different from you, that's all. Not so strong, maybe, not able to cope without someone to lean on. I used to wonder what it was that attracted him to my mother when he could have had his pick of plenty of women, but when I saw them together I began to understand. I know Mum gives the impression of being scatty and disorganised, and she is in some ways, but that doesn't matter to Gerald; in fact it makes him feel needed. But there's a warmth with Mum, an essential desire to give of herself that a lot of people just don't have, and your father needs that, Declan.'

His face was still carved in stone and she hunted for something, anything that might get through the impenetrable wall. 'I don't care how many women he had had since your mother died; her loss was still affecting him very deeply when he met mine. He could have had a blonde bombshell, a status symbol hanging on his arm, he's a rich and very attractive man, but he wasn't into that, was he? What were the other women like that he went out with—young, sexy?'

She had gambled her argument on her instincts and now waited with bated breath for him to answer.

He stared at her for a long moment without replying and she couldn't read his face at all, but she was having her own problems fighting the impulse to throw herself into his arms and smother his face with kisses, to try and take away all the pain, all the hurt. She breathed deeply and waited.

'No...no, they weren't,' he admitted slowly at last. 'They were...' He paused, and now she had the feeling he wasn't seeing her any more, that he was searching back in the past for something that had eluded him for years. 'They were his age or older,' he said softly with a strange note in his voice. 'Ordinary even, I guess. I always wondered why, when my mother had been so outstandingly beautiful. What they had that she didn't.'

'They didn't "have" anything,' Paige said quietly. 'But he needed comfort, understanding, and he was searching for it in the only way he knew how. My mother told me once that there are still nights when he murmurs your mother's name in his sleep. He loved her, Declan. He loved her very much. Don't ever doubt that.'

They stood in total silence for a full minute as he continued to look down the years, his big body frozen and his mind obviously far from her. She could see his face working but had no idea what he was thinking, how her words had penetrated the bitterness of days, weeks, months, years of heartache. She had the sudden mad impulse to take him in her arms, but she fought it.

'No,' he said suddenly. 'I don't believe it.' He was speaking more to himself than to her but she answered anyway.

'Why not?' she asked softly. 'You know your mother believed he loved her; can't you see that she would have known if it were as weak a love as you thought?' Her eyes reached out to him.

'But it wasn't like that,' he said distractedly. 'I would have understood——'

'At fourteen?' she said quietly. 'A fourteen-year-old boy who has just lost the mother he adored is looking for perfection in his father, fair or not. You were hurting and he was hurting, but because you've always found it difficult to communicate you misunderstood the path he took to get through the best he could.' Her voice vibrated with feeling.

'No.' He stared at her as though he hated her. 'No. You don't know him as I do.'

'Can't you forgive him for being human?' she asked softly.

'Can you forgive that?' he asked tightly.

'I've never judged your father,' she protested in surprise.

'I wasn't talking about my father,' he said coldly. As she looked into the silver eyes she saw a deep fury darkening the normally impassive face and forced herself not to flinch from it. This was a backlash, a reaction against what she had said.

'From the first moment we met you took an instant and quite unreasonable dislike to me which you have fed religiously throughout the years. At our parents' wedding there was sheer hate shining in your eyes when you looked at me, Paige—can you deny it?' She stared at him silently and he gave a short harsh laugh. 'No, I thought not. And this feeling has been nurtured to the point where you are blind to the truth. Today was a perfect example. You assumed I was encouraging Corinne in her less than noble aspirations even though I put her in her place several times throughout the day, to the embarrassment of Margaret and Eric, I might add. But *you* wouldn't notice because you don't want to. You were such a little slip of a thing at sixteen, Paige; can't you even begin to acknowledge that an irrational childish vendetta should have been discarded along with the pigtails?'

'It wasn't irrational.' She spoke without thinking and it served only to heighten his fury.

'So you admit I was right?' he asked with menacing quiet. 'You dare to lecture me on the way I've failed my father when all the time——'

'You don't understand.' Her voice was harsh now with a mixture of pain and fear. Half of her was tempted to tell him the reason for her defiance and withdrawal through the years, but somehow she couldn't bring herself to say the words. The humiliation had gone too deep to be voiced aloud. He must think what he wanted. She couldn't tell him the truth.

'I understand only too well,' he said bitterly. 'You think of me as less than an animal in that determined little mind of yours. I disgust you, I can see it in the way you shrink from any contact, and yet you can't deny the way I can make you feel physically either. It must be galling that someone you despise so completely can excite you.'

There was something in his tone and the stiffness of the big body held so rigidly taut in front of her that warned her he was on a knife-edge. She didn't understand why her opinion of him should matter so much when the only emotion it had seemed to arouse in the past was one of mocking cynicism, but he wasn't satirical now, and as she stared into the glittering eyes she doubted if he ever had been. But then she wouldn't know, would she? Paige reflected miserably. She didn't understand him at all. And herself still less.

'I don't despise you, Declan,' she said carefully.

'No? Hate, then, loathe? Just different words for the same emotion.' His voice was infinitely weary.

'Not that either. Can't we stop this fighting, perhaps try to be friends?' She suddenly realised that she wanted that desperately. 'You said once——'

'Friends?' He stared at her as though she had asked for the moon. 'I can't be *friends* with you, Paige!

Don't you see——?' He stopped abruptly, running a shaking hand through his hair as he groaned deep in his throat. 'I can't believe this is happening to me, not at my age.'

'What's happening?' He was talking in riddles and yet it was important; she knew it from the note of pain in his voice that he couldn't quite disguise.

'It doesn't matter.' He glanced at the expensive gold watch on his wrist and shook his head. 'I shall have to be going if I want to catch that plane.'

'But you can't go,' she said desperately without realising what she was saying. 'We haven't got anything settled yet—your father, everything.' He couldn't just go?

'My father.' The words were dead. 'To be honest, Paige, right at this moment I couldn't care less about my father or your mother or anything else. I know it's important to you that I make things right with him, for both their sakes, but if I'm truthful I'm concentrating on *me* and catching that plane without making a bigger fool of myself than I have already.'

'A fool of yourself?' She stared at him uncertainly, her huge greeny brown eyes reflecting her bewilderment. 'But you haven't ... Oh, you mean about your mother?' She gave a tentative smile. 'But you were just saying how things were, surely? How can that be——?'

He swore, softly and succinctly, as he reached forward and took her in his arms and just for a second she was too surprised to react. One hand was tangled in the red silk of her hair, steadying her head for the penetrating invasion of his mouth, and the other was a rigid band round her waist holding her immobile in his arms. His lips were hard and fiery as they forced hers open to enable his tongue to explore the soft inner flesh of her mouth, lighting an immediate response she couldn't hide, but his body cradled her close with a fierce kind of tenderness as though he needed to absorb her into his very being, devour her into the stark essence of him until she was utterly immersed in his maleness.

It was violent and consuming and yet tender, and she found herself racing in a hot, sensory intoxication that was as frightening as it was thrilling. The control had all but gone for the second time, but now his mouth was warm and sensual against her lips as his hands roamed where they would. Somehow her hands had found their place in the crisp darkness of his hair as she reached up to the broad, tense shoulders, and as he felt her touch his hungry arousal became shockingly obvious as he pulled her into him so tightly that she could feel every inch of his muscled body against hers, his mouth groaning her name ravenously.

Paige knew it was up to her to put the brake on, but somehow the revelations about his boyhood and the bitterness he had revealed had melted something deep inside her that had been the pivot of her resistance, and now she was helpless against his passion and her own weakness.

As they sank to the floor together she was conscious of one moment of sheer panic and then it was gone, lost in the feel and smell of him, the overwhelming need his body couldn't hide. His mouth was hot and insistent, but then the ache that his lovemaking had aroused was shattered as the harsh, shrill tones of the telephone directly over their heads exploded her back into the real world with shocking abruptness.

Declan froze totally and then moved off her in one swift motion that brought him upright, snatching the phone off the hook and speaking into it in a sharp, clipped voice that was at odds with his shaking hands. As she sat up slowly he replaced the receiver and turned to lean against the wall with his back to her, both hands resting against its smooth outline.

'Declan?' Her voice was a broken whisper in the stark silence that had fallen and for a moment she thought he hadn't heard her, but then he moved slightly, the bunched muscles in his shoulders flexing as his head dropped further.

'You see how it is?' he asked tonelessly. 'You're playing with fire, Paige.'

'Fire?' She glanced up at his broad back as she rose to her feet, finding her legs would barely support her.

'Yes, fire,' he snarled softly, turning to face her, his eyes glittering grey in the stark whiteness of his face. 'Keep away from me, Paige, do you understand?'

'But I thought——'

'It's for your own good.' He interrupted her shaking voice with a brusque shake of his head. 'I know you think I've no principles at all, but, surprisingly, there are still a few I adhere to. One of them is that the women I make love to know the score and want it as badly as me. With you it's different.'

She stared at him, her hazel eyes the only live things in her face. 'Different? Why?'

He looked at her for a long, long time in the shadowed hall as the old grandfather clock ticked away in a corner and she wondered at the play of emotions that crossed his face, but then he sighed deeply, his eyes closing against her.

'You don't like me, Paige.' He laughed humourlessly. 'And who can blame you? We both know I'm no innocent but that's exactly what you are. I couldn't believe it at first but you're an infant, a baby where a man is concerned. The fact that I could seduce you is of no credit to me, and the fact that I want to, even less. Now just go.'

'Go?' she repeated the word disbelievingly.

'Now!' This time his voice bit into the air with such ferocity that her legs moved in spite of herself, and as she stumbled into the drawing-room she shut her eyes as she sank down on the sofa. The glow from the Christmas tree lights combined with the dusky grey settling on the garden made the room seem infinitely cosy when she opened her eyes again after some minutes, in spite of the high ceiling and opulent furnishings. Cosy and safe and sheltered. The exact opposite of what she was feeling inside, an emotion so raw that it was grinding into her chest with a physical pain. How had her life got into this mess? She glanced round the room vacantly. Just a year ago she had been her own person, happy, secure and knowing exactly what she wanted out of life. And now? The question mark made her wince with pain. Now she didn't know herself any more.

She heard the car start outside without believing at first what she was hearing, but after sitting in stunned silence for a moment she leapt up and ran to the front door just in time see a swirl of silver roar out of the drive and disappear from view. He had gone? He couldn't have. She stood staring down the pebbled drive, empty except for the bare trees and tidy clean lawn swept clear of winter debris by the cutting wind that had piled the dead leaves against the old stone wall bordering the grounds. Just like that? Without a word of... A word of what? She leant back against the wall of the house and took deep, unsteady breaths of the icy air. A word of comfort? A word of tenderness? But that didn't apply to them, did it? She turned abruptly and walked into the warmth of the house, shutting the door so violently that its bang vibrated the floor.

Later that night, after Gerald and her mother had arrived home happy and glowing, she escaped to her room to sit in silent contemplation of the dark cold garden for hours. It was after midnight when she heard the phone ring and muted voices in the hall.

'Paige?' Her mother's light knock at her bedroom door caught her unawares and she found herself flying into bed in the same manner as when she was ten years old and had heard adult footsteps on the stairs when she had been playing with her doll's house instead of being fast asleep under the covers.

This time, though, her agitation was to save her mother the worry of finding her only daughter pale-faced and wan as she wept for she knew not what. 'Paige, are you awake?' Brenda's voice was a soft whisper as she peered round the door after a moment. 'Declan's on the phone.'

When her mother had left, assuming she was asleep, and all was quiet again, Paige found she was dry-eyed at last, but with a strange kind of guilty emptiness taking hold of her that was more excruciating than anything that had gone before.

Why had he phoned? She curled up into a tight little ball under the covers as her stomach twisted in a giant knot. Probably with a carefully prepared explanation to smooth things over now that he was happy and satisfied in his own world again. And she wouldn't have been able to bear a second brush-off. She twisted wretchedly. But she only had herself to blame. She had let those few words that he had spoken six years ago colour her opinion of him until she had been blind to the real man. She had painted him black—no grey, no tinge of shading to lighten the image—and now there was a chasm between them which was quite uncrossable.

And she would have liked to get to know him. Even as she let her mind voice the thought, his words came back to her in painful clarity. 'You're playing with fire…you're an infant, a baby.' He clearly didn't want to get to know her! She twisted restlessly again. And why should he? Apart from the insults she had thrown at him at every occasion, the barely concealed dislike and aggressiveness, she just wasn't his type. His women were sophisticated, worldly-wise and totally free spirits who played the game and then went on to the next man with a smile and no hard feelings. Could she ever be like that?

No, she couldn't, she admitted to herself honestly. But just at this moment in time she wished with all

her heart that she had been made differently. She had
lost even the brief contact she had with him now. She
didn't know why it mattered so much but it did.
'Guilt?' She spoke out loud into the empty room.
'Well, you might have been an idiot, Paige, but he's
no angel.'

It was bleak comfort. He had gone without even
saying goodbye, and that said it all.

CHAPTER EIGHT

'PAIGE?' Matthew's voice was gentle as he faced her over the small table for two in the lush restaurant. 'Who is he?'

'What?' She stared back into the handsome boyish face in surprise as her stomach gave a tremendous lurch. It had been hard getting back into the swing of things when she had arrived back at her small flat after the Christmas break five weeks ago but she had thought her misery was well concealed, and the odd friendly, no-strings-attached date with Matthew had broken the monotony of endless evenings spent huddled over the drawing-board as her mind refused to concentrate on the task in hand.

'There's someone who's put those shadows under your eyes.' Matthew touched her face lightly. 'You love him, don't you? Is it Declan?'

'Please, don't be so ridiculous!' She took a big gulp of the dry white wine that had accompanied the baked trout and tried a light laugh that failed miserably. 'Declan?' she questioned shrilly. 'We don't get on, Matthew, we never have; in fact the only feeling we seem to generate between us is abject loathing.'

'It is?' Matthew settled back in his seat as his eyes roamed across her flushed face. 'Well, I'm not one to argue, as you well know, but I'd bet my last fiver that the look in his eyes that day at your parents' house was not dislike. Far from it, and excuse me for saying so, but you seemed to be pretty aware of him too.'

'Matthew, leave it, please.' She ran a shaking hand across her mouth before taking another huge sip of wine. 'You don't understand. We've never hit it off, but there does seem to be some sort of physical attraction there. It means nothing. Less than nothing.'

'OK, Paige, have it your own way.' Matthew let the subject drop with his customary good humour. 'But just remember, this shoulder is broad and always available, and I don't like to see you so down. Now——' he indicated the menu with a wave of his hand '—a slice of that cheesecake you like so much here?'

How she got through the rest of the evening she didn't know, but she was conscious of herself talking and laughing and saying the right things while that inner self looked on as a silent spectator. There was a big question in her mind that she didn't dare let take shape, and while Matthew was with her she could keep the ghost at bay, but the second he left her flat a few hours later, after a nightcap she had deliberately prolonged, she had to face the fact that her brain had been screaming at her ever since Matthew's concerned enquiry. She loved Declan.

She loved Declan? 'No!' She slung the coffee-cups and brandy glasses into the sink with such force that the resulting splintering crash was inevitable. 'I don't!' She stared at the wall angrily. 'I won't let myself be so stupid.'

She paced the flat furiously, telling herself that Declan was the last man in the world to love. Totally self-sufficient, needing and wanting no one, and yet...

Her traitorous mind would remind her of those moments in his arms, of his fierce tenderness, the odd moments of vulnerability, all the small things that made up the whole. And there was his mother. She found she could no longer keep the thoughts at bay. He had clearly adored her and suffered for her with a sensitivity that most teenage boys would have been incapable of. But the fact remained that love spelt weakness, betrayal and ultimate disappointment to Declan, and his world, with its smooth glass walls and impersonal, dispassionate little boxes into which each area of his life was slotted with detached neutrality, was what he wanted.

She got ready for bed slowly, lingering under the shower for some time as she let the warm water mingle with the tears on her uplifted face. She had always loved Declan; it was time to face facts. The knowledge had been tucked away deep in her subconscious since that troubled summer when she was sixteen and he had hurt her so badly. All the resentment, bitterness and anger had been intensified because of that weakness she had fought so strongly, a desperate bid to kick against the pricks. She didn't want to love him, she wasn't even sure if she liked him most of the time, but it had been *fait accompli* from the first moment he had teasingly tousled her hair and she had looked up through her thick horn-rimmed glasses to see his dark, mocking face smiling down at her.

'You're Brenda's kid?' She still remembered their first exchange of conversation. 'Don't look so scared, tich, this lot won't eat you.'

'I'm not scared,' she had lied bravely with another tiny glance at Gerald's well-to-do friends, and Declan had chuckled softly.

'You aren't? Good for you! Most of them scare the hell out of me.'

She had asked his name then, and after introductions had been completed she had tagged along with him for the rest of the afternoon until that catastrophic return to the house when she had overheard his conversation with Gerald. How would things have been if Gerald hadn't told him that day that he intended to marry her mother? She closed her eyes for a moment as she leant weakly against the side of the shower cubicle, and then shook her head slowly. What did it matter after all? What was done was done. Life had made Declan what he was, and fate had thrust her into his orbit at the worst time possible, colouring every future meeting. She had been crying for the moon for years without having the courage to admit it to herself, and, now she had, it was time to get on with the rest of her life, armed with her new knowledge. Declan would never love her, but maybe, through their parents, they could learn to be friends. It was as much as she could hope for, and better than nothing. She would never allow herself to be just another brief affair, even if it meant a solitary life married to her career, but perhaps, just perhaps, she could be the one woman in his life who offered an unconditional friendship that as they grew older could become a port he made for in the storm of life. It was second best, but all there was.

She lay in bed with her head spinning and her brain buzzing with a thousand words. After an hour of tossing and turning she flung the covers aside and reached for pen and paper. She would write to him. Casual, friendly, explaining that their last meeting had been a mistake she was sure he regretted as much as she and that, if only for their parents' sake, it would be better to see each other now and again in the future, to try and behave as far as possible like two mature adults whom fate had placed in the same family. She didn't want him to stay away, she would tell him. Once the letter was written, addressed care of her mother, she felt better, and it wasn't until it had been posted the next morning that the misgivings blossomed. They lasted for a few days, but then routine blurred the edges and she threw herself frantically into her work, allowing no time for thought or troubling self-recriminations. She knew he would find the letter embarrassing, difficult to handle, and he would almost certainly ignore mentioning it in the future, but if it just allowed them to visit Brenda and Gerald at the same time without either one of them having to avoid the family home it would be worth it.

It was as she was working on a particularly difficult sketch one evening at the flat two weeks later after a supremely trying day that the shrill chimes of the doorbell broke her concentration. Swearing softly under her breath, she marched tightly to the door and swung it open with a ferocious scowl darkening her countenance.

'Hi, there.'

If the ground beneath her feet had opened or a choir of heavenly angels had begun to sing she couldn't have been more shocked as she stared into Declan's wary, unsmiling eyes.

'Is there any particular reason for the scary face or do you usually greet callers with such charm?' he asked mockingly. 'You didn't know I was calling, so in this instance at least I assume it's nothing personal?'

'Declan!' She stared at him helplessly, quite unable to move from the spot. He looked very big and very dark, and her stomach twisted with the force of her love.

'Paige!' he answered softly in the same tone. When she still didn't move the dark face grimaced slowly, his eyes narrowing as a little gleam of amusement warmed their depths. 'Do we stand here all night saying each other's names, or am I permitted into the sanctuary?' he asked drily.

'Oh, I'm sorry.' She stepped backwards so quickly that she almost fell over the doormat. 'Come in, please; it's just so unexpected...' Her voice trailed away as the thudding of her heart didn't lessen. 'I didn't know you were coming.' She heard herself babble with a feeling of helplessness that bordered on panic. He looked so good.

'No.' As he stepped into her tiny hall the silver gaze remained fixed on her face. 'I should have rung, I suppose.' The hard mouth lifted slightly at one corner. 'I could say it didn't occur to me but it wouldn't be true. I thought if I rang you might put me off, make some polite excuse, or maybe in your case not quite so polite.' His voice was very dry. 'Would you have seen me?'

The question was so direct that for a moment she couldn't speak, and when she did it came out all wrong. 'Seen you? Of course. I wouldn't turn anyone away, I never have.' She stopped as she realised she was babbling again.

'Could I have a cup of coffee?' He obviously realised he wasn't going to get much sense out of her, she reflected miserably as he took her arm and ushered her through into the living-room. 'I've driven straight here and the meal on the plane seems like a year ago.'

'Driven straight here?' She walked through to the tiny kitchen and noted with a pang of dismay that he had followed her. There was barely enough room to swing a mouse, let alone a cat, and he suddenly seemed very close and very attractive.

'With a quick stop at Hertfordshire,' he said blandly, but not before she had noticed a quick flare of colour under the dark cheekbones. The letter? He'd read the letter. Her stomach turned over in anticipation.

'But you should have eaten or at least had a drink before driving again,' she said faintly, her mind buzzing.

He looked at her for a long moment and then to her relief turned and strolled back into the living-room, his voice muted slightly through the open door. 'I thought you might not have eaten as it's still quite early,' he said in answer. 'Have you?'

'No, I don't think so.' She realised that that sounded incredibly stupid and made a tremendous effort to pull herself together. He would think she was stark staring mad! 'I mean, not since lunch,' she corrected more firmly.

'Good.' He appeared in the doorway again and she caught her breath at the sight of him. The big black overcoat he wore seemed to emphasise his dark masculinity still further and his hair had been slightly tousled by the wind. He looked big and powerful and dangerously attractive, and as she hastily poured two cups of coffee from the coffee machine she left switched on all day she took a long, deep breath to still her trembling hands. He was here. In the flesh. Now! 'Would you care to go out for a meal? I see you're working; I hope I haven't interrupted anything.' The silver eyes stroked slowly over her hot face.

For a whole millisecond she considered being casual and offhand, making some light throwaway comment and then smiled brilliantly. 'I'd love to, absolutely love to,' she said quickly.

He blinked slightly at her enthusiasm as he took the coffee she offered, but the dark face was unreadable as they walked through to the living-room and sat facing each other over the small coffee-table strewn with her work.

'I think we need to talk, Paige,' he said softly after a long, tense pause.

'Yes.' She stared at him hungrily, wishing he didn't look so good. It was all very well having noble intentions regarding their future relationship when the image of him was confined to her mind, but now he was here in the flesh the situation was subtly different!

'I don't find it easy to express my feelings,' he continued quietly. 'I never have. Hence the rush tonight. Once I'd made the decision to see you on the plane I wanted to carry it through before I lost my nerve.'

'Oh.' He'd decided to see her before he read the letter, then? And he hadn't mentioned it. She *had* embarrassed him, she knew it; she should never have written it. Had he guessed how she felt? She'd die if he had.

'I don't want us to be enemies, Paige.' The silver eyes were very clear as they fastened on her flushed face. 'It's the last thing in the world I want.'

'Neither do I.' She was desperately trying to pull the shreds of her tattered pride together. 'It makes things impossible for Mum and Gerald, after all.' Keep it casual, make it easy, a separate part of her mind instructed tightly.

'Brenda and Father. Yes. I see.' The controlled voice was giving nothing away and she could read nothing in the enigmatic face in front of her. 'Do you think it's possible, feeling about me the way you do?'

'Feeling about you . . . ?' For an awful moment she thought he had guessed the truth and then his hard bite of a laugh indicated differently.

'This antagonism, dislike, call it what you will.' He sat back in the chair and stretched out his long legs as he spoke and just for a second she thought she saw an expression of infinite weariness in the clear grey eyes. 'You can't have changed that much in a few weeks.'

I haven't changed in years, she thought painfully, and I don't think I ever will. He looked tired, drained, and she would have given the world for the freedom to go and sit by his side and trace the lines of exhaustion with her lips, but that was less possible now than it had ever been. 'I think it's time to put personal feelings aside,' she said carefully, 'and besides, I don't dislike you, Declan. We just seem destined to strike sparks off each other, that's all.'

'That's all?' There was a faintly brooding expression on his face that could have meant anything. 'But do you think you can manage to keep up the pretence of happy families for long?'

'No, not pretend.' She had answered more sharply than she would have liked and tried to moderate her voice as she continued. 'Can't we agree to differ on the way we see certain things? Relationships, lifestyles...' Her voice trailed away at the wry gleam in his eyes.

'Is there anything left we *do* agree on?' he asked sardonically as he stretched suddenly, standing up in one fluid movement that belied the weariness and moving to the large window that overlooked a host of undulating rooftops, dark and tranquil in the cold night. 'I understand what you're saying, Paige,' he said quietly after a time as he stood with his back to her, looking out into the city skyline. 'And for the record it's very noble of you to be so reasonable, especially after our last meeting.'

'Declan——'

'No, please.' He raised his hand authoritatively as she would have interrupted him. 'I know you don't

like me, but it would seem you are prepared to try
and find some common point of contact. And I agree.
Our respective parents are owed that much at least.'
There was something in the cool male voice that
caught at her heart-strings, but she couldn't have explained why. A note of pain? Of uncertainty? No, she
was imagining things, as she always seemed to do
around this man. She couldn't trust her natural
emotions where he was concerned; she doubted if she
ever would be able to. 'Well?' He turned suddenly
and the lazy smile gripped at her stomach. 'Are you
coming for that meal? I think there's a smudge of
charcoal on your nose, incidentally.'

'Really?' She raised her hand quickly and backed
towards the doorway. 'I won't be a moment. Help
yourself to another coffee.'

Once in the safety of her bedroom she realised she
was shaking uncontrollably, and sank down on the
bed with a feeling of helpless longing. Now she had
admitted her feelings to herself they seemed to have
intensified a thousandfold. How on earth was she
going to get through the evening, not to mention the
rest of her life, feeling like this? She rested her hot
face against the cool glass of the dressing-table mirror.
He had looked tired. Was he working too hard? She
shook herself irritably. That was just the sort of thing
he would loathe if she voiced such a concern. He
would look on a love such as hers as a heavy chain
round his neck. She raised her head to stare at herself
in the glass. But he was here *now*. And it was a start.

By the time she left the bedroom ten minutes later
she looked cool and beautiful on the outside even if

the inside was a trembling mess. She walked with studied casualness into the lounge, only to see that the exercise was wasted. Declan was fast asleep on her tiny sofa, his dark head lolling back against the flowered cushions and his long legs stretched out tiredly in front of him. She stood for a moment in the doorway, feasting her eyes, her new awareness taking in every little minute detail of him that she might have missed in the past.

She noticed a tiny, very old scar just to the right of one eye. A childhood accident, perhaps? A cricket ball that had gone astray? And the hair that he always raked back so severely was slightly longer than usual, as though he hadn't had time to get it cut, and she noticed a tendency to curl in its thick strands. And the eyelashes. So thick and long as they lay on the hard, finely planed cheekbones. She put her arms round her waist and hugged herself suddenly as a shaft of pain swept through her. She loved him, she loved him so much. What was she going to do?

He stirred suddenly, as though her scrutiny had reached him even in sleep, and she backed out of the doorway, calling his name in the tiny hall just before she re-entered the lounge. 'I'm ready! Sorry to have kept you waiting.'

He was still draped in the same position but his eyes were open now, their silver light holding her gaze as she looked over to him. 'You look lovely,' he said slowly as he sat upright, his glance taking in the plain wool black dress that was elegant as well as functional and the high loose knot on top of her head secured with a black velvet ribbon. 'If I had known you were that rare entity of a woman who doesn't take a couple of hours to get ready I'd have taken you out before now.'

'Would you now?' She tried to match his lightness. 'Well, now you know what you've been missing, don't you?'

'I think I've known that for a long time,' he said enigmatically as he stood up to help her on with her coat. His touch burnt her through the thick coat and she had to steel herself not to shiver at his closeness, but she managed it, just. If this new tentative relationship was going to mean anything she had to be cool and calm, with just the right amount of warmth to make the offer of friendship believable. It was the only way she could be different from all the others.

As they drew up outside the hotel and an attentive doorman moved forward to open her door Paige glanced at Declan in open amazement. 'Here? We're going to eat here?' It was one of the most exclusive hotels in London, and certainly one of the most expensive. 'Have you booked a table?'

'No.' He glanced at her from the corner of his eyes as he prepared to leave the car. 'But I know the manager. There will be a table.'

'Good evening, Mr Stone.' The doorman smiled widely as Declan handed him the car keys. 'Miss.' He nodded to Paige who smiled back vacantly. 'Are you staying with us, sir?'

'Not this time, Bob,' Declan replied easily. 'It's just a fleeting visit, but I couldn't think of a restaurant I like better, so...'

'Thank you, Mr Stone. *Bon appetit.*' The small man was grinning from ear to ear as he climbed into Declan's silver car, handling the vehicle with an aplomb that spoke of familiarity, and as another doorman greeted Declan by name Paige glanced at him curiously.

'I take it you stay here when you're in London?' she asked quietly.

He nodded slowly as they entered the foyer, an expensive arcade of shops that catered for the wealthy guests at the hotel oozing names that made her breath catch in her throat. 'It's convenient,' he said shortly. 'I gave up my flat years ago, preferring just one home in America. Makes life simpler.'

'Yes, it would,' she murmured drily as he drew her over towards the breathtakingly smart restaurant that was alive and glittering with beautiful chandeliers, exquisite mirrors and opulent furnishings that vied with the famous clientele. Paige recognised at least two celebrities before she had even sat down at the small table for two close to the intimate little dance-floor, and the number of beautifully dressed women made her glad that although her dress wasn't exactly glamorous it made her feel good.

This, then, was his home from home! She felt a sad, wry pain catch at her heart-strings as the last clinging hope that she could ever mean anything more than a friend died a swift death. He lived on the same planet but in a different world! Her eyes clouded although she kept her expression bland. These women, with their fabulous jewels and voluptuous beauty— if they couldn't tempt his heart of stone, why did she

ever harbour the secret desire that she could? Because
that was what she had been doing! She smiled grimly
to herself. And she had convinced herself she had
written the letter in friendship! She felt such a savage
anger with herself for a second that she could have
screamed. She was such a fool.

'You're doing it again.' His voice was cool and very
sardonic.

'Sorry?' She glanced up to find the grey eyes firmly
fixed on her face.

'Giving the impression that you're in the company
of the devil himself.' He reached out a hand and tilted
her face upwards to look more clearly into the wide
hazel eyes. 'Try, just for this evening, to look as
though you are enjoying my company?' There was a
small throb in his voice that spoke of some inner
emotion but she was too embarrassed to notice. 'Now
here's the waiter. Smile nicely and agree with everything I say.' He was acting as though he was amused,
but she sensed suddenly that the opposite was the case.

'I'm sorry, Declan, I didn't mean——'

'And no apologies,' he said softly, his eyes unreadable. 'I am tired of either apologising or being
apologised to. Now, pineapple and melon cocktail
followed by lobster? Yes?' At her nod he smiled at
the waiter who had materialised at their side. 'And a
bottle of my usual wine, please, Claude.'

The courses came and went, but Paige wasn't conscious of what she ate at all. Her whole being was
concentrated on the dark, cold face opposite. Declan
was his usual imperturbable, cynical self, composed
and self-possessed, hooded eyes slightly closed as he

gazed now and then round the room. She noticed he
didn't eat much, as though he was under some strain,
but then maybe he had business problems, she thought
worriedly. Her mother had confided that she thought
he was under some pressure when she phoned a couple
of days ago, divulging that Gerald was a little concerned about his son. Perhaps he needed to talk to
someone?

'Is everything all right, Declan?' she asked on impulse as they sat lingering over coffee, his face distant
and aloof.

'All right?' His eyes snapped to her face instantly
and his face had taken on an alert, watchful look.
'Why do you ask?'

'I don't know,' she floundered hesitantly. She
mustn't let him think she was giving him the third
degree; it would be the last thing he would want from
a woman. 'You just seem a little preoccupied, not your
usual self.'

'Not my usual self.' He repeated her words slowly,
smiling crookedly. 'And what, in your opinion, is my
"usual self"?'

She stared at him silently, not at all sure what he
wanted to hear, and he frowned slightly, a darkness
clouding his eyes.

'I'm not going to bite your head off, Paige,' he said
tautly, 'so stop looking scared to death. You can talk
to me, you know, I am flesh and blood.' She opened
her mouth to speak but the words died as he leant
forward suddenly, taking her hand in his and staring
down at its slenderness lying in his large palm.

Neither of them said anything for a full minute, and then he sighed softly as he very gently placed her hand on the table before leaning back in his chair again. 'To answer your question honestly, no, everything is not all right,' he said expressionlessly, 'and you are quite right, I am not my normal self. OK?' She couldn't quite discern the smile he gave.

'What's wrong?' she asked carefully, feeling her way slowly. 'Business problems?'

'Not exactly.' He looked at her tightly. 'Why the concern? Not that it's not appreciated, of course.' His voice was the old Declan, full of mockery. 'But it's so unexpected.'

'Can I help at all?' she asked quietly. He looked at her for a long moment, his body quite still, and as she held his gaze she felt her heart begin to pound madly. There was an expression in his eyes that defied description, a mixture of pain, bewilderment, bitterness and a strange kind of hunger that made her breath stop. He was hurting badly, she could feel it, but he wasn't going to let her in, she could feel that too. Was it a woman? Now her breathing accelerated so fast that she felt dizzy for a moment. Had a woman finally got to him at last? Not now, she prayed silently as she wrenched her gaze away from his. I could stand it later perhaps, but not now.

'Love trouble?' She kept her voice light and her head lowered and he would never know the effort it cost to talk so naturally.

'Just so.' The deep voice was laconic. 'And you?' He paused but for the life of her she couldn't raise

her head and look into his face at that moment in
time. 'How's Matthew?'

'Matthew?' Just for a crazy moment her brain
wouldn't function and she wondered who on earth
Matthew was. 'Oh, Matthew—I think he's fine, I
haven't seen him in days.' He's fallen for someone,
her head was screaming. One of those elegant,
sophisticated beauties that populated his world.

'Why not?'

'Why not?' She stared at him blankly. She couldn't
remember what she had just said.

'Why haven't you seen Matthew in days?' Declan
asked patiently, his silver eyes glittering oddly.

'Oh, I've been busy, he's been busy—you know how
it is,' she said faintly. What was she like? Blonde,
brunette, a sultry redhead?

'Yes.' He answered her in a strangely abstracted
tone, his gaze dropping to her mouth and lingering
there for a infinitesimal moment before he turned to
the waiter who had appeared at his elbow. 'That was
excellent as always. Could you arrange for the car to
be brought round?'

'Of course, Mr Stone.'

As he rose from his chair and moved to her side,
placing his hand beneath her elbow, she tried to match
his coolness, but the trembling that even such a casual
touch ignited swept through her in a slow shiver.

'Cold?' He looked down at her quickly.

'Not really,' she said huskily. His gaze sharpened
but he said no more, helping her into the car that was
waiting for them outside without a word. He drove
as he always drove, fast and smooth, and in the few

minutes it took to reach her block of flats Paige toyed with the idea of inviting him in for a nightcap. She was torturing herself, she knew that, having him so close but so far, and if he started to talk about this other woman . . . Her mind raced on. But she didn't know when she would see him again, and she couldn't bear to let him go yet.

'Would you like to come in for a coffee, brandy or something?' she asked lightly as he brought the sleek silver car to a halt in the car park at the back of the flats.

'Thank you.' His smile jolted her heart again and she lectured herself fiercely all the way to her front door. Probably the only reason he'd decided to clear the air with her in the first place was because he was on Cloud Nine with this new love and could afford to be generous. She felt a stab of pain so strong that it caught the breath in her throat. She had lost something she had never had in the first place and suddenly, faced with the knowledge that he was beginning to care for someone else, all her high ideals and motives seemed pathetically empty.

Should she have taken the sort of relationship that would have evolved if she had allowed their love-making to develop to its natural conclusion? No. Even as the doubts surfaced she knew she had had no choice. She couldn't have had him, loved him for however long it took for the physical attraction he felt for her to be sated, and then let him go without it destroying her. She had to face facts. She just wasn't the type . . . his type.

'Here, let me.' She was fumbling with her key, his presence making her all fingers and thumbs, and as he opened the door and they stepped into the tiny hall he put his hand on her arm, drawing her round to face him as he kicked the door shut with the back of his foot. 'Paige?' The rough edge to his voice and the darkness in the silver-grey eyes brought her heart to her mouth. 'Paige, I need to tell you, you have to under-stand——'

The telephone's shrill ring made her jump violently and his grip loosened at the same time as a wry twist curved his mouth. 'Saved by the bell.'

'Did you need saving?' she asked uncertainly as she reached for the phone and his low growl of a laugh caught at her breath.

'Not me, honeypot, you.'

'Hello?' As she spoke into the receiver she was aware of a slow trembling starting in the pit of her stomach as he moved to stand behind her, drawing her against him as he stroked the back of her neck in a whisper-light caress.

'Paige?' Matthew's voice was loud enough for Declan to hear. 'It's Matt. How are you, sweetheart?' It was his usual form of address and meant nothing, but as Declan stiffened and moved away she knew he had misunderstood the affection in Matthew's voice. He's embarrassed, she thought apprehensively, at eavesdropping, albeit unintentionally.

'Fine, Matt.' As Declan walked into the small lounge she took a long, deep breath. Hurry up, Matt, please, she thought weakly.

'I feel I've been too busy to keep an eye on my favourite girl,' Matthew said lightly. 'How are you sleeping—better?'

'Stop worrying,' she said softly, appreciating the concern but not the timing.

'What are friends for?' Matthew's voice was gentle. 'Someone has got to keep an eye on you!'

'And you do it very well,' she countered with a wry smile, 'but now is not the time.'

'Company?' Matthew asked warily. 'Oh, no, Paige, don't tell me it's Declan? It's not, is it?'

'Yes.' She heard him groan with a mixture of exasperation and concern. 'I'll see you at work, OK?'

'OK.' The phone went down quickly and she could almost see him put his hand to his brow.

'You needn't have cut it short on my account,' Declan said icily as she joined him in the tiny lounge. He had been standing with his back to the room looking out of the window and now as he turned she saw his face was cool and withdrawn. 'I'm sure you two have lots to talk about, having missed a few days.'

'Not really.' She looked at him blankly. 'He just——'

'He's about your age, isn't he?' Declan continued as though she hadn't spoken. 'You obviously have a lot in common—work, friends and so on.'

'I suppose so.' She could feel the coldness coming off him and was at a loss to understand the sudden change of mood. 'Matt's a good friend.'

'I'm sure he is,' he said curtly as he glanced at the gold watch on his wrist. 'It's later than I thought, Paige, I'd better take a raincheck on that coffee.'

'Oh, but——'

'Goodbye.' He barely glanced at her as he left the flat, his body tight and rigid and his profile enigmatic as he passed her. She stared after him blindly as the door swung shut with a final click, the abruptness of his departure causing a sensation of actual physical sickness. What had she said wrong? What had she done? She had wanted to ask him when he was going to be in England again, to arrange—— Her thoughts stopped dead. Arrange? Arrange what?

When are you going to get it through your thick head that you mean nothing to him? she asked herself bitterly. She was a vague member of his family through necessity, that was all, and now there was someone else in his life who would make absolutely sure she held on to what she had, or she would if she had any sense, Paige corrected painfully. The look in his eyes had been blinding, shocking in its intensity. This was one woman who wouldn't be discarded along with the rest.

As the tears came, hot and fierce, she wished with all her heart that she could hate him, but it was too late. Far, far too late. The saddest, loneliest words in any language.

CHAPTER NINE

THE next few days crawled by, and Paige had never been more thankful that she had a job which demanded total concentration. It didn't ease the excruciating ache that had her heart in an iron grip, but there were times when it was dulled enough for her to function normally.

The only bright spot in the darkness was a telephone call from her mother the day after Declan's visit to her flat. 'Paige?' Her mother's voice had been questioning and a little sheepish. 'Did Declan call to see you last night?'

'Yes.' Paige shut her eyes tightly. She couldn't answer any questions or discuss Declan this morning, not even for her mother.

'Did he seem different to you at all?'

'Different?' Paige asked warily as she breathed out slowly. 'In what way?'

'I don't really know,' her mother said softly. 'It's just that he came here on a lightning visit and left Gerald with a smile that stretched from ear to ear. They were in the study the whole time and I don't know what was said exactly.' Her mother had the grace to sound bashful. 'All Gerald will say is that some old ghosts have been laid to rest. Do you know anything about it?'

174

'Nothing,' Paige said firmly as her heart thudded violently against her ribcage. He had made his peace with Gerald! And of course Gerald wouldn't want to hurt her mother by reiterating his love for his first wife. Maybe her words had got through to Declan after all, but no... She caught herself quickly. It was far more likely that his new love had persuaded him to see things from a different angle. An unbiased, clear viewpoint from an outsider would carry more weight than anything she could say, and she could still picture his outrage on the day they had discussed things.

'Oh, well...' Her mother's voice was disappointed. 'I suppose I'll never know, then.'

'I should think it's probably some indiscretion of Declan's in the past that he needed to get off his chest,' Paige said comfortingly, wanting to put her mother's mind at rest. 'Gerald would feel he was betraying a confidence if he discussed it with anyone, I suppose, and if it helps the pair of them get closer it doesn't really matter, does it?'

'No, you're absolutely right, darling.' Brenda sounded happier at once and Paige gave a tired smile into the receiver. There were times when she felt years older than her mother! 'Gerald is still on Cloud Nine today, and apparently Declan is coming to spend Easter with us this year—that's good, isn't it?'

'Great.' If Paige's voice lacked the necessary enthusiasm her mother didn't notice.

And so the days dragged on. When the telephone rang at five one morning a week after she had last seen Declan, she groaned softly as she reached out for the receiver. Yesterday had been a bad day; his face had materialised on the paper every time she had settled down to work and it had been gone one in the morning before she was satisfied with the designs she had struggled with all day.

'Paige?' The voice on the other end of the line was unmistakably Declan's and she sat bolt upright in bed as her heart galloped frantically.

'Declan?' She took a deep breath. 'How...how are you?' she stammered helplessly. What was the time-difference with America? Was it night-time there? Was he with anyone? Why was he ringing? He cut off her racing thoughts abruptly.

'I'm fine.' He didn't sound fine. Even with all the miles separating them she could sense the note of anguish in his voice. Had his new love ended it? She felt a moment's fierce longing that she had and then felt bitterly ashamed of herself. It wouldn't make any difference to their relationship anyway, so why hope? 'I've got some news I thought you might like to hear.'

He was getting married! She had heard the expression of blood running cold, but it was the first time in her life that she had actually experienced the phenomenon. It wasn't pain she had read in his voice, but excitement. 'Yes?' Even to herself her voice sounded dead.

'Are you alone?' The sudden note of uncertainty in his voice didn't register until after she had replied in the affirmative.

'Of course I'm alone, it's five in the morning.'

'Yes, of course.' There was a thread of something she couldn't fathom in the sombre voice. 'You just sound a little strange.'

'You woke me up with a jolt,' she said quietly. Get on with it, Declan, she thought numbly, get it over with in one swift blow.

'It's my job,' he said grimly. 'Good news.'

'Your job?' For a second the relief was so overwhelming she felt faint. 'Promotion?'

'And how.' The note of uncertainty was still there and she wondered why he didn't sound more pleased. 'I thought you might be interested to know, after the letter?'

'The letter?' What on earth was he on about? she thought helplessly. Why mention the letter now?

'The letter you wrote to me. Brenda forwarded it to my hotel from Hertfordshire. I've just read it.'

'You've just read it.' She was repeating his words again, she thought desperately, confusion making her voice blank. He'd only just received the letter, then?

There was silence for a few seconds and then his voice was infinitely weary when he next spoke. 'It doesn't matter. I just thought——' He stopped abruptly. 'The job will involve moving permanently to Canada for a few years, so you'll have some peace at last. This dislike, antagonism, call it what you will— you'll be free of its burden. You won't have to pretend for our parents' sake after all.'

'Declan?' She hesitated, frightened of saying the wrong thing. All her instincts told her he was probing, searching, inviting her to say more, but the past as well as the present held her in its grip. He had crucified her at sixteen and continued to hurt her ever since, and now that there was someone else—how could she bare her soul to this man? If he even suspected her true feelings for him she would die. Her pride was the only thing she had left.

'Why, Paige?' Now his voice wasn't cool or reserved but raw with pain. 'I've got to know. Why do you hate me so strongly? What is it in me that you find so hard to take?'

'I don't hate you, Declan.' She heard herself say the words with a strange feeling of calm and knew she was going on to explain in spite of the power such an admission would give him. She suddenly realised that there was nothing to lose any more; her pride was unimportant beside the hurt in his voice. She had to set things straight, explain, and then maybe at least he would understand what had motivated her in the past. Anything was better than this giant tangle.

'I don't hate you,' she repeated slowly, 'although I thought I did once. But you hurt me, you see, and it was some sort of defence mechanism, I think, although I've only realised that recently. You remember the first time we met at your father's home? When he held the barbecue to introduce my mother to his friends?' As she continued to explain the ripples that that one conversation overheard so innocently on a fine summer's evening had made in their lives, there was a deathly silence on the other end of the line. As she brought the story up to the present she found she couldn't tell him of her love for him. If he had made some comment, anything, it might have been easier, but the blank silence tied her tongue into knots and fed the growing suspicion that she was making a terrible, ghastly mistake.

'Declan?' As her voice stumbled to a halt the silence lengthened, and as she heard the receiver replaced at the other end her stomach jolted with a shock of rejection. She had bared her soul, almost, and for what?

'Declan!' As she threw the receiver down in agonised disbelief the momentum caused the rest of the phone to follow it into a crashing heap on the floor, and while the jarring sound faded she sat staring vacantly into space, struggling to believe that he hadn't offered one word of comfort, of apology, of remorse. She didn't know how to cope any more with the pain that was tearing her apart, the searing knowledge that he cared for her so little, that she was so unimportant. She had really believed that she could stay on the perimeter of his world, waiting, hoping, trying to make him trust her, but she saw now it was useless. He was crushing her, slowly and relentlessly, just by being himself, and unless she put him out of her life completely, cauterising the wound in whatever way it took, there would be nothing of herself left.

She sat rocking aimlessly on the bed, the pain too deep for tears, and after a long time rose slowly like an old woman and walked through into the kitchen to make a cup of coffee.

The ring at the doorbell didn't surprise her; she felt as though she had fallen into a kind of vacuum where nothing would ever surprise or move her again, and she didn't even wonder who was calling at six o'clock in the morning as she padded into the hall and opened the front door.

'Paige?'

Slamming the door in Declan's face was instinctive but he reacted just as quickly, stopping it with his foot as he moved forward. 'You're in America,' she whispered brokenly. 'You phoned me from America.' She backed away from him as he advanced, a tumult of emotions playing over her face, her eyes wide and confused. 'You said the letter had been sent——'

'Paige?' He reached out and shook her gently. 'What on earth is the matter? Did I frighten you? It's me, I'm not in America. I said the letter had been sent to my hotel, here in England, in London.'

'Did you?' She took a long, hard, deep breath as she tried to pull herself together. The shock of seeing him like that had temporarily robbed her of her wits. 'But it's so early. I thought——'

'If I hadn't phoned then I'd have lost my nerve.' He ran a hand distractedly across his face as he stepped back a pace towards the still open door, and she noticed he was very white. 'I've just got in from Heathrow and thought I'd open my post before I had a shower.' The silver eyes were strangely unguarded, more intense than she had ever seen them. 'I needed to talk to you, damn it, don't you understand?' He shook his head at her blank expression, a touch of cynical humour touching his mouth for a moment. 'But no, of course not, why should you? You really don't have any idea how I feel, do you?'

'How you feel?' She tore her gaze away from his as she looked down at her bare feet, letting her cloud of red silky hair hide her face from his. 'I think I know how you feel, Declan,' she said wearily as the irony twisted her heart.

'I doubt it.' The deep voice was husky. 'But I want you to do one last thing for me and listen while I talk to you, try to make you understand about the past, everything. And then I'll get out of your life, for good. Is that a deal?' His voice cracked painfully.

She looked up then, her face as white as his, and nodded slowly. 'You'd better come and sit down.' He followed her into the lounge after shutting the door but didn't sit down, pacing the small floor as he began to talk, his voice low and even, belying the bitter pain and harshness in his face.

'I know this will make no difference to how you feel about me, Paige, but I must explain.' She curled her feet under her as she huddled in the soft armchair, pulling the belt of her dressing-gown more tightly around her waist and drawing its long folds over her feet, which were ice-cold.

'That night at the barbecue, when you heard me talking to my father——' He stopped abruptly, his face ashen. 'Hell, Paige!' He stopped his pacing to face her. 'You must believe I didn't mean a word I said, even then. I was angry and hurt and furious with Gerald for letting my mother down yet again, and I just lashed out blindly. I didn't mean the things I said about your mother or yourself; in fact I'd thought how sweet and shy you were, so different from most of the crowd there. If I'd have known you heard me...' He drove one hand into the other in a clenched fist and then resumed the pacing.

'I hated myself afterwards for what I said that night. Can you believe that?' He paused and faced her directly and, looking into the tortured eyes, she nodded slowly.

'Yes, I believe you.'

'But Father and I had never got on, and within weeks he had given me an ultimatum. Accept Brenda completely or get out of his life. I chose the latter.' He shook his head at the memory. 'Crazy really, and so like both of us. I'm more like him than I care to admit. But I was filled with a strange kind of hate-love for him. Hate at the way I felt he'd let my mother down, and love for him as my father. But I couldn't have even put it into words then, it was buried too deep, until——' He stopped suddenly. 'Until you made me face it.'

'Me?' Her voice was very small.

'Yes, you,' he said gruffly. 'You made me realise that I had spent a good deal of my adult life running away, from normal life, commitment, love... And all along I'd got it wrong. Misjudged things totally.'

He knelt down in front of her chair and her stomach muscles clenched at his closeness, at the familiar intoxicating smell of his aftershave and the gleaming darkness of his hair as his head came down on a level with hers. 'I've been a blind fool, Paige, and all the time I thought I'd got it together, that I was where I wanted to be.'

'You did?' She knew she should be saying more, but the shock of seeing him like this had robbed her of all thought; even her throat seemed to be in the grip of this dazed unreality that was paralysing her reactions.

He nodded slowly. 'I've wasted endless years chasing success and living the life of a western nomad, terrified of putting any roots down, of establishing ties. I chose my women for their sophistication in the game of love, for their ability to be as cool as I was. None of them touched my heart, Paige. Not until——' He looked at her tightly.

This was it, she thought painfully. This was the moment of truth about the other woman. Would she be able to bear it? No, not from his own lips, not now like this. She sprang up so suddenly that he almost stumbled before he straightened. If she heard it from Gerald or her mother she might just be able to cope without making a terrible fool of herself.

'I'm glad you came to clear the air, Declan,' she said frantically fast, her face distraught as she walked to the door. 'And I'm thrilled you went to see Gerald—Mum phoned and told me. That's all your loose ends tied up and you'll soon be gone, won't you, to a new job, a new life . . . ?' And a new woman, her mind finished wildly.

He stood very still for a long moment, his face grey and strained and his eyes brilliantly silver, and then as she turned to face him covered the ground between them in two steps. As he took her into his arms she was too amazed to react, but then, as she felt his heart beating wildly and the fierceness of his lips as they ground on to hers, her mind stood still. It was a long, deep kiss and her head was swimming when he raised his head, his face impassioned and bitterly sad.

'One last thing to forgive me for.' He stepped back a pace as she swayed in front of him. 'But it's got to last me a long, long time. There'll never be anyone but you, Paige, but you don't want to hear this.' He shook his head in violent disgust at himself. 'You've made it clear how you feel about me, and I of all people know that physical attraction doesn't last too long. Maybe you don't even feel that any more.'

She stared at him, her eyes huge in the whiteness of her face and her hand to her lips that were bruised with his kiss.

'You'll never know how you affected me that night I opened the door and saw the girl of my dreams standing there,' he said huskily, a harsh twist to his lips that caught at her heart. 'And then I got to know you and the hell of it was, the dream was real. I'd never imagined that someone like you still existed in this crazy world. But I knew all along there was no chance. Even if you hadn't loathed me on sight, you deserve someone like Matthew, who hasn't been contaminated by life the way I have. And I love you enough to stay out of your life. I promise you that.'

He had left the flat and reached the lift doors before her stunned senses made sense of it all, and as she called his name they closed on his face, so cold and unapproachable that she wondered for a second if she had just dreamt the last few minutes.

'Declan?' As she spoke his name into the empty corridor she realised he had done it again—left her before she could speak to him, tell him how she felt. 'Declan!' She was pounding her fists on the closed doors when a dry cough behind her brought her back to herself.

'Is there anything wrong, Miss Green?' She didn't even bother to reply to her next-door neighbour's disapproving enquiry, flying back into her flat and slamming the door before tearing her dressing-gown off in an agony of haste.

Was he at the hotel he had taken her to? He had to be! He *had* to be. She couldn't have explained how she felt as she dressed in frantic frustration at her own slowness, her heart thudding and her head spinning and the tears running down her face in a flood that was quite unstoppable. He loved her. *He loved her*! It was insane, impossible, and the enormity of what it meant was beyond her but she knew she had to get to him, fast. He was quite capable of carrying through the grand sacrifice he thought he was making and leaving the country before she even had a chance to talk to him. How could one man be so impossibly blind, utterly infuriating and altogether wonderful?

When she reached the still deserted London street outside there wasn't a taxi to be seen, and as she began to jog along the path, her eyes scanning hopefully for one of the cheerful cab drivers who usually could be relied on to be around, the absurdity of the situation struck her. In all her dreams, when she had imagined Declan falling in love with her, she had never contemplated this finale. And maybe he hadn't returned to the hotel. What if he had called in to see her on the way to the airport? The icy trickle of doubt that crept down her spine stirred her feet to greater speed and now, giving up all hopes of a taxi, she fairly flew along the pavements, her heart pounding.

By the time she reached Declan's hotel she had realised she was more than a little out of condition, although, she reflected ruefully as she leant against the railings opposite the grand building, perhaps a mile-long hike first thing in the morning with no warning was a little extreme for anyone! When she had regained sufficient breath and composure to enter the huge foyer she found she was shaking and took a few deep breaths as she glanced around. Everything was calm and hushed.

'Can I help you?' The girl who appeared at her elbow looked incredibly fresh and smart for so early in the morning and Paige felt even more like a fish out of water as she looked into the cool, smiling face, eyebrows carefully raised in polite enquiry.

'I'm here to see Mr Stone, Declan Stone,' she said with all the assurance she could muster. 'I was here with him a few weeks ago. I'm his stepsister.' She didn't know what made her add that last sentence, but as she did so the beautiful face took on a degree of warmth and the girl's smile relaxed into a genuine welcome.

'Of course.' She smiled brightly. 'Is he expecting you?'

'Not exactly.' Paige kept her voice firm and confident. 'I was rather hoping to surprise him, actually.'

'Oh.' The smile faltered a little. 'Well, I really ought to ring through to his suite, Miss . . . ?'

'Green, Paige Green,' Paige answered automatically. 'Do you have to? I promise it will be all right.'

'Well, if you're sure . . .' The girl's eyes ran over Paige's thick warm jumper, sensible trousers and flat

shoes and seemed reassured. She obviously wasn't the
type wicked women were made of, Paige reflected
ruefully. 'He's in his normal suite,' the cool voice
continued, 'third floor.'

'Thank you.' Paige smiled with all the calm she
could muster and made for the lifts, wondering what
she was going to do when she reached the third floor
if there were several different doors.

'Third floor, miss.' The liftboy smiled at her as the
doors slid open.

'Thank you.' She hesitated. 'Which are Mr Stone's
rooms?'

'End of the corridor, miss.'

There was no answer to her knock and the sense of
anticlimax was painfully frustrating. She tried again,
harder and longer this time, and then the door swung
open and there he was. He'd obviously just stepped
out of the shower, a light towelling robe ending just
above his knees and his hair dripping wet.

'Declan!' As she flung herself into his arms they
opened instinctively to receive her, but after the first
heart-stopping moment of being held tightly against
his broad chest she felt a shudder run through the
muscled body as he carefully pushed her to arm's
length.

'Why are you here?' That he was exercising su-
preme self-control was evident in the fact that the
words had been forced through clenched teeth and
the big body was taut and still. 'You shouldn't have
come, Paige, there's nothing more to be said.' The
mask was very firmly in place, she noted dispassionately, as she took in the veiled cold eyes, straight

mouth and hard, tight face, but for once the guise didn't intimidate her. She had seen the real Declan a short while ago and she was going to reach him regardless of the old barriers so firmly in place.

'I disagree,' she said quietly as she moved past him into the sumptuous room beyond. 'In fact I seem to remember it was you who did all the talking. I never got a word in edgeways.'

'Paige, I think you'd better leave.' As she turned to face him the stony façade hadn't faltered. 'If you've come to offer words of sympathy I can do without them.'

'Words of sympathy?' She stared at him hard. 'You are the last person in the world I would ever pity, Declan.'

'What, then?' She saw the flash of uncertainty that coloured his eyes cloudy grey for an instant before he recovered himself. 'Your pound of flesh, is that it?'

'You could put it like that.' She moved forward to his side, reaching up a hand and stroking the hard face as she did so. 'But I want all your flesh, Declan, not just a pound.' She smiled her love into his eyes.

She saw the disbelief in his face along with something that made her want to cry as she went up on tiptoe to kiss his mouth, and then his hands had come out to hold her to him in a bear-hug that left her unable to breathe. 'Paige? Paige, is this real? You aren't playing with me?' As his tortured voice whispered in her ear, she strained even closer into his body in reply.

'I love you,' she said into the warmth of his throat before raising her head and raining tiny frantic kisses on his face. 'I always have. I loved you the minute I set eyes on you at sixteen and I've been trying to fight it ever since.'

'Don't fight it.' His voice was husky as his arms tightened still more round her slim shape, lifting her off her feet. 'Don't ever, ever fight it, my love. Loving you the way I do has turned my world upside-down and nearly killed me, and if you wanted revenge you've had it a million times since that night at the birthday party. I've nearly gone mad night after night, imagining you in Matthew's arms or, worse still, someone I didn't know about. I've been living in hell with no hope of release ... Oh, Paige ...'

Long, satisfying minutes later he raised his head to look down into her glowing face, his eyes dark with passion. 'Marry me? Soon?'

'How soon?' she breathed shakily.

'Special licence soon?'

She nodded happily. 'Nearly soon enough. But in the meantime ...'

FREE
GOLD PLATED BRACELET

Mills & Boon would like to give you something extra special this Mother's Day—a Gold Plated Bracelet absolutely *FREE* when you purchase a 'Happy Mother's Day' pack.

The pack features 4 new Romances by popular authors—Victoria Gordon, Debbie Macomber, Joanna Neil and Anne Weale.

Mail-away offer — see pack for details.
Offer closes 31.5.94

Available now   Price £7.20

MILLS & BOON

IS PASSION A CRIME?

WORLDWIDE

A sizzling
novel of
romantic
suspense

HOT ICE

NORA ROBERTS

Reckless and beautiful,
Whitney MacAllister had
the cash and the connections.

Streetwise and good-looking,
Douglas Lord had the
stolen documents leading
to a fabulous hidden fortune.

It was a business prop-
osition—pure and simple.
But the race to find the
treasure, from Manhattan
to Madagascar, was only
part of the game.

*Don't miss Nora
Roberts' sizzling novel
of red hot passion and
cold hard cash.*

W☽RLDWIDE

AVAILABLE NOW   PRICE £2.95

HEARTS OF FIRE

By Miranda Lee

HEARTS OF FIRE by Miranda Lee is a totally compelling six-part saga set in Australia's glamorous but cut-throat world of gem dealing.

Discover the passion, scandal, sin and finally the hope that exist between two fabulously rich families. You'll be hooked from the very first page as Gemma Smith fights for the secret of the priceless **Heart of Fire** black opal and fights for love too...

Each novel features a gripping romance in itself. And **SEDUCTION AND SACRIFICE,** the first title in this exciting series, is due for publication in April but you can order your FREE copy, worth £2.50, NOW! To receive your FREE book simply complete the coupon below and return it to:

**MILLS & BOON READER SERVICE, FREEPOST,
P.O. BOX 236, CROYDON CR9 9EL.   TEL: 081-684 2141**

NO STAMP NEEDED

Ms/Mrs/Miss/Mr: _____ HOF

Address _____

_____

_____ Postcode _____

mps
MAILING
PREFERENCE
SERVICE